Williamsburg ®

Reproductions

CRAFT HOUSE
COLONIAL WILLIAMSBURG
WILLIAMSBURG, VIRGINIA 23185

CONTENTS

WILLIAMSBURG REPRODUCTIONS PROGRAM

Domestic furnishings in eighteenth-century Europe reached a high level in design and quality. It was a time when skilled craftsmen designed and fashioned both utilitarian and decorative objects. The skill of the artisan, the quality of the tools, and the available materials resulted in the finished product. Furniture, looking glasses, silver, brass, pewter, fabrics, wallcoverings, chandeliers, glass, dinnerware, all having been brought into the colonies, had a profound influence on the colonial craftsmen. They, in turn, designed and crafted objects, often possessing a distinctive American character.

For over fifty years Colonial Williamsburg's curators have assembled one of the largest and most distinguished collections of seventeenth-, eighteenth-, and early nineteenth-century English and American furnishings in this hemisphere. Archaeological discoveries, inventories, wills, deeds, letters, diaries, and shipping invoices influence the decision for most of the acquisitions. Specialists continue to expand this collection as well as their own knowledge of the arts and social life of the period. They work from an enormous body of cumulative data to insure the continuing validity of furnishings likely to have been in Virginia before and after the American Revolution, or, more specifically, in the historic buildings of Williamsburg.

Behind the thousands of items in the Colonial Williamsburg Collection is a mass of data to lend authority and authenticity to the original pieces and thus to items in the reproductions program. Guidelines that govern the program permit articles to be made within three definitive areas, Reproductions, Adaptations, and Interpretations.

REPRODUCTIONS

In the early 1930s Colonial Williamsburg opened to the public the Capitol, Governor's Palace, and Raleigh Tavern. The Raleigh Tavern was furnished with many objects based on broken fragments found in the excavations of the tavern site, such as ceramics and glassware. The response of visitors to the building was immediate. They wanted to know how they might obtain accurate reproductions. Colonial Williamsburg then considered the possibility of turning to its rapidly expanding collections to select a number of items based on criteria of beauty, soundness of design, and appropriateness for daily use in modern American homes. They foresaw that carefully-made reproductions would serve to extend the educational endeavors of the Foundation. Subsequently, a few prominent manufacturers, with both the resources and desire to produce fine reproductions, were chosen. All were responsive to the educational aims of the Foundation. Reproductions were to bear the Colonial Williamsburg hallmark. In 1937, Craft House opened to serve as the public display and sales area for items made in the Colonial Williamsburg Reproductions program.

Those who purchased a reproduction wing chair, tea table, ceramic or glassware object can now look back with great satisfaction. The article has not only served well, but also has provided beauty to the household and is a constant reminder of the fine qualities of eighteenth-century design and craftsmanship. The reproduction likely influenced the taste for other selections in the home. A purchase made in the late nineteen thirties will soon be fifty years old, and, it might be said, an heirloom in its own right.

How does Colonial Williamsburg determine the selection of an article to be reproduced? The process begins by first consulting the Department of Archaeology to learn if fragments have been found at a given location. A study is then made of the collection and generally two or more similar items are selected initially. The manufacturer then studies the items. Often, handwork or techniques used in the original are not practical for a reproduction because tools, and even materials, have changed throughout the years. Once the article has been agreed upon, it must be thoroughly documented as being of the period. The object is then carefully studied and followed during the reproduction process. Many accumulated and specialized techniques are employed in reproducing each article.

Once a prototype has been completed by the manufacturer, the reproduced article is presented to Colonial Williamsburg's Products Review Committee, for approval. The committee consists of many talents within the Foundation, including the directors of archaeology, collections, research, as well as the reproductions program. After considerable critical analysis, the committee either approves, disapproves or suggests revisions for resubmission at a later date. Finally, when the item has been approved, the manufacturer is consulted and, if in agreement, production begins. This process usually takes a year or more to complete.

The reproductions are so strikingly similar to the originals that it may tax the layman's eye to detect a difference. Craft House occasionally displays the antiques alongside their counterparts to emphasize the close

Facsimile of Certificate of Authenticity that accompanies each hallmarked reproduction

resemblance. The Reproductions Program has been highly successful through the years and a number of the original manufacturers continue to participate nearly fifty years later. Currently there are over twenty-five manufacturers licensed by the Colonial Williamsburg Foundation, producing a total of over two thousand items.

ADAPTATIONS
Like Williamsburg reproductions, adaptations are crafted with the same care and attention to detail. For this reason, they bear the Colonial Williamsburg hallmark. These items are referred to as adaptations for they have been altered in some manner from the original antique. A good example would be fabrics and wallpapers: the document, from which the design was fashioned, usually was available in only one coloration. To suit the needs of

today's tastes, the design is produced in a variety of color adaptations. A pewter bowl, for example, has an original size, but because of the popularity of design, is offered in size adaptations. Arms are sometimes added to side chairs to effect a dining setting. In every case, however, changes follow the style in which, it is judged, they would have been modified at the time the original was crafted.

INTERPRETATIONS
Interpretive items fill an educational, as well as practical, need for visitors to Colonial Williamsburg. Visitors often seek a small gift item as a remembrance or souvenir from Colonial Williamsburg. These articles, also approved by the Products Review Committee, often relate directly to the Historic Area, such as children's mob caps and tricorn hats, coloring books and continental flags. Electrified articles, furniture of

modern construction. commemoratives, note cards and kits to make period items all fall within this classification.

CRAFT HOUSE
All of the products in this catalogue are approved by the Colonial Williamsburg Foundation and have been made by specially selected manufacturers. Selections may be viewed and purchased at Craft House, Williamsburg, Virginia, or ordered from this catalogue for prompt delivery. Supplement prices include shipping and handling charges unless otherwise noted. Careful attention is given to all orders.

Craft House also stands ready to answer any specific questions you may have about items in the Williamsburg Reproductions Program. Experienced decorator assistance is offered.

WILLIAMSBURG SHOPS
This catalogue and most Williamsburg products are available in Williamsburg Shops in a number of leading stores in the country. Williamsburg Shops are operated by the stores in close cooperation with Colonial Williamsburg and its licensed manufacturers.

DECORATORS AND SPECIALTY GIFT SHOPS
Many leading decorators and home furnishing and specialty stores, offer Williamsburg reproductions and adaptations, in addition to Craft House and Williamsburg Shops. Decorators who specialize in period furnishings are in a position to be of help in the selection of interior paints, rugs, fabrics, wall coverings, and furniture for your home or office. Call on them, for they like to work with Williamsburg Reproductions.

WILLIAMSBURG AND THE HALLMARK

"Williamsburg" and the hallmark, both registered trademarks owned by the foundation, may be used only on reproductions and adaptations made by licensed manufacturers. The Williamsburg hallmark, shown above was designed from old and new symbols. The letters "C.W.," for Colonial Williamsburg, have been joined to the central symbol, an elongated "4" ending in what appears to be a double "X." This symbol was used by English

shippers of the 17th and 18th centuries and was sometimes combined with the initials of merchant and consignee.

Origins of the merchants' and makers' mark are obscure and possibly ancient. One legend has it that the mark traces back to the Greek god Hermes, patron of commerce and trade, in whose honor the symbol "4" was worshipped. The double "X", according to one theory, symbolized man looking up to a benevolent god. Yet another theory

is that the symbol "4" is of runic origin—that its past is buried in the unwritten and little-known history of early European alphabets. Some scholars suggest that it might have been intended as a sign of the cross. Whatever its origin, this central symbol has appeared on merchandise of quality for centuries and continues today in the hallmark for the Colonial Williamsburg Reproduction Program.

Many products in the Colonial Williamsburg program are displayed and sold in fine stores throughout the United States, as well as at Craft House.

Selections may be purchased at Craft House or ordered from this catalogue for prompt delivery. Careful attention is given to mail orders, instructions for which may be found on page 285.

LICENSED MANUFACTURERS FOR THE WILLIAMSBURG REPRODUCTIONS PROGRAM

ARMS
Navy Arms Co., Inc.
689 Bergen Blvd.
Ridgefield
New Jersey 07657

BEDSPREADS
Bates Fabrics, Inc.
1431 Broadway
New York
New York 10018

BLANKETS
Naturally British
P.O. Box 347
Alexandria
Virginia 22313

BRASS & IRON
Virginia Metalcrafters
1010 East Main Street
Waynesboro
Virginia 22980

CLOCKS
Chelsea Clock Company
284 Everett Avenue
Chelsea
Massachusetts 02150

CRYSTAL & DELFT
Foreign Advisory
Service Corporation
Princess Anne
Maryland 21853

DINNERWARE & CERAMICS
Josiah Wedgwood & Sons
41 Madison Avenue
New York
New York 10010

FABRICS
F. Schumacher & Co.
919 Third Avenue
New York
New York 10022

FIGURINES &
CHARACTER JUGS
Doulton & Company, Inc.
P.O. Box 1815
Somerset
New Jersey 08873

FIREPLACE EQUIPMENT
The Harvin Company
Box 500
Waynesboro
Virginia 22980

FURNITURE
Kittinger Company
1893 Elmwood Avenue
Buffalo
New York 14207

LEATHER
Lackawanna Leather Co.
P.O. Box 1008
Conover
North Carolina 28613

LIGHTING FIXTURES
Virginia Metalcrafters
1010 East Main Street
Waynesboro
Virginia 22980

LOCKS
Folger Adam Company
P.O. Box 688
Joliet
Illinois 60434

MINIATURES
Plaid Enterprises, Inc.
P.O. Drawer E
Norcross
Georgia 30092

MIRRORS
Friedman Brothers
Decorative Arts, Inc.
9015 N. W. 105 Way
Medley
Florida 33178

NEEDLEPOINT &
NEEDLEWORK
Johnson Creative Arts
(Elsa Williams, Inc.)
445 Main Street
West Townsend
Massachusetts 01474

PAINT
Martin Senour Company
1370 Ontario Avenue, N. W.
Cleveland
Ohio 44113

PAPER PRODUCTS
Charles Overly Studio
Old Littleton Road
Harvard
Massachusetts 01451

POTTERY
Williamsburg Pottery
Factory, Inc.
Route 3, Box 148
Lightfoot
Virginia 23090

PRINTS
The Dietz Press, Inc.
109 East Cary Street
Richmond
Virginia 23219

PUBLICATIONS
Colonial Williamsburg
Williamsburg
Virginia 23185

RUGS & CARPETS
Karastan Rug Mills
919 Third Avenue
New York
New York 10022

SILVER, SILVERPLATE,
& PEWTER
Kirk Stieff Company
800 Wyman Park Drive
Baltimore
Maryland 21211

SOAP & FRAGRANCES
Caswell-Massey Company
575 Lexington Avenue
New York
New York 10022

STATIONERY & NOTES
Sheaffer-Eaton Textron
75 S. Church Street
Pittsfield
Massachusetts 01201

WALLPAPER
Katzenbach & Warren, Inc.
950 Third Avenue
New York
New York 10022

WOODEN ACCESSORIES
Virginia Metalcrafters
1010 East Main Street
Waynesboro
Virginia 22980

WILLIAMSBURG FURNITURE REPRODUCTIONS AND ADAPTATIONS

About the time Williamsburg was founded in 1699, most people were sitting on stools and benches, not chairs. The furnishings of our first colonists were crude and few. But a change was stirring, and the 1700s witnessed a revolution in demand for home furnishings. For the first time that demand came not just from the limited upper classes. It also came from a rising and numerous middle class who were newly experiencing the benefits of comfortable homes. This was true in England and it was certainly true of the American colonies. In Virginia the tobacco planters had grown wealthy; it was they who initiated the steady consumption of fine articles. Prosperous townsfolk were not slow in following their example.

The "furniture revolution" began in England with the return of Charles II and his more open Court, influenced by the manners and arts of Versailles. Plain Cromwellian chairs gave way to spiral turnings and elaborate carvings. William and Mary brought in Dutch craftsmen and European baroque design. But the greatest period was to begin in the short reign of Queen Anne and to run through Georgian times to the early nineteenth century.

American colonists, tied to England by blood and trade, bought this furniture, copied it in their own workshops and made it their own. Today a Queen Anne chair of the period, made in America, is as authentic (and expensive) as one made in London.

Virginia's tidewater planters bought furniture in London and had it delivered to their doorsteps by the tobacco ships. The citizens of Williamsburg furnished their homes, taverns, and public buildings with imports, but soon were buying American pieces from New England, Philadelphia, and later from Baltimore. Such treasures constitute the present furnishings and collections of Colonial Williamsburg. They provide the pattern and examples for *Williamsburg* Furniture Reproductions and Adaptations.

Colonial tastes followed, at a little distance, the growing sophistication of the imports. At first, articles of the previous century were still in vogue: a chair of Charles II with a cane back; or a William and Mary dressing table. Often a style would long outlive the monarch for whom it is named.

Gradually, without displacing the old, new styles appeared. Soon after the middle of the century the products of Mr. Chippendale were all the rage, and his publication *The Gentleman and Cabinet Maker's Director* became a bible for some English and colonial cabinetmakers. This was the peak of the highly decorated, rococo style: natural objects like shells and foliage were carved in wood, along with motifs from the Gothic and Chinese. Thomas Chippendale's name has been applied to furniture of every description: the comfortable (and draft-proof) wing chairs, the elaborate breakfronts, the elegant sofas. He was the inspiration for a New England-built tall post bed, a Philadelphia lowboy and a New Jersey highboy. All these Chippendale pieces are represented in the Williamsburg collections; they, in turn, are faithfully reproduced or adapted to serve in traditional and modern decors alike—for "modern" is always relative.

The capital of Virginia was moved to Richmond in 1780, and, as a result, Williamsburg ceased to be the center of political and social activity it had been during the previous three-quarters of a century. Not unexpectedly, population declined and prosperity waned, but the town did not fold up and die. In fact, several of the largest and most attractive houses surviving in Williamsburg today date from the last decades of the eighteenth century and the early years of the nineteenth. Among these are the Semple House on Francis Street, built before 1782, which was described in 1807 as "the handsomest house in town;" the rambling St. George Tucker House, constructed principally between 1788 and 1795; the brick Norton-Cole House on Market Square built between 1809 and 1812; and the spacious Coke-Garrett House near the Public Gaol, which was built in the nineteenth century, except for the eighteenth-century west wing.

While undoubtedly some of the furnishings of these newly constructed houses were in the earlier styles of the eighteenth century, by the 1790s examples of the new, classically inspired furniture styles popularized by Hepplewhite and Sheraton were to be found in Williamsburg. For this reason Colonial Williamsburg has acquired pieces of Federal furniture and accessories made before 1830, the generally accepted date for the beginning of the machine manufacture of furniture. Many of these items were chosen to furnish rooms in the Coke-Garrett House, now the official residence of Colonial Williamsburg's president. Each reflects the delicacy and lightness so characteristic of the Federal style, relying for its beauty on simplicity of line and form, embellished with exciting contrasts of inlay and veneer, rather than on the ornate curves and heavy carving of the preceding Chippendale style. This enables Colonial Williamsburg to present a broader interpretation of life in Williamsburg, extending beyond the colonial period into the exciting early years of our national history.

Throughout these periods of change the American workmen followed their English compatriots' lead and also developed their own modifications. A tall post bed made in New England in the late eighteenth century and now a *Williamsburg* Reproduction is nevertheless immediately recognizable as Hepplewhite in style with its slender tapering posts finished off with delicate finial urns.

In mid-century the beautiful and durable American mahogany achieved pre-eminence in English furniture making; it was shipped to England in vast amounts and mahogany became the touchstone of fine furniture. Sometimes mahogany veneer was used when especially decorative and matching wood effects were sought. The mahogany tradition is integral to the Colonial Williamsburg Reproductions and Adaptations Program. The combination of fine woods, hand workmanship and fine period design produced products that were eagerly sought after; their use for two centuries is witness to their essential durability.

Adaptation of these pieces to modern living is a matter of taste and subtlety. It may take two forms: first, a scaling down to meet the space and ceiling dimensions of the modern apartment. Yet oddly enough, while some adaptations have been scaled down, others had to be scaled up. We have actually "grown" since the eighteenth century and for real comfort our dining tables are now made an inch higher than theirs.

Also modern homes call for interpretive items as coffee tables, unknown to Chippendale and Hepplewhite. An eighteenth-century butler's tray is the inspiration for a sturdy and adequate coffee table in the Chippendale tradition. In another interpretation, the bench section of a Queen Anne day bed made in Rhode Island in 1740 provides an ample low table for use in a drink-and-conversation setting.

Truly eighteenth-century and early nineteenth-century taste has found an echo in the twentieth century's demand for elegant, decorative, and eminently practical articles of furniture.

Craftsmen at work in the Anthony Hay Cabinetmaking Shop.

PERIODS AND STYLES OF FURNITURE

English furniture styles take their name either from the reigning monarch—Charles II, Queen Anne, George II, etc., or from the great designers who appeared as a veritable galaxy in the last half of the eighteenth century—Thomas Chippendale, the brothers Adam, George Hepplewhite, and Thomas

Sheraton, whose names are immortalized in their furniture designs. These styles were taken up, sometimes promptly, sometimes with a time lag, by American craftsmen. Partly this was due to transportation delays, partly to a hesitation to switch to "new models" before the public taste was ready to accept them.

As far as England was concerned, the eighteenth century was characteristically "Georgian" and the successive periods closely match the reigns of the four Georges. In America, the dominant styles were (in modern terminology): "William and Mary," "Queen Anne," "Chippendale," "Hepplewhite," "Sheraton" and "Federal." The *Williamsburg Reproductions Catalogue* carefully attempts to convey as much

information as possible as to the date and style of a given piece of furniture, and its origin, whether from England or from a center in the original colonies.

The chart below shows the reigning periods of the monarchs and the approximate times when a given style enjoyed its peak of popularity, both in England and in the colonies.

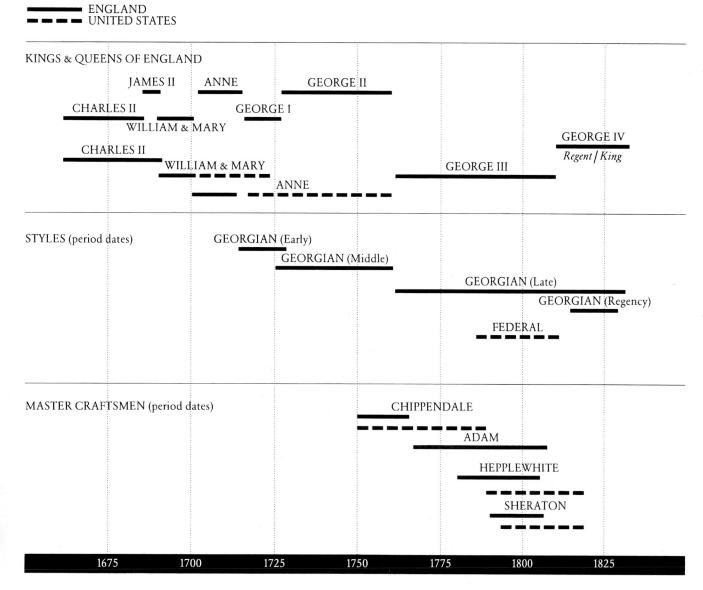

CHARLES II

When Charles II was called to the throne in 1660, England joyfully shed the spartan austerity of the Cromwell period. Returning from exile on the Continent, the court brought with it an air of luxury and elaborate manners. The rectilinear lines of Cromwellian furniture were replaced with elaborate designs from the Continent. Deep carving (1) and spiral turning on legs and stretchers (2) appeared. Oak was gradually supplanted by walnut.

Flemish scroll feet were used on chairs, tables, and bed terminals (3); cane chairs made their first appearance (4). Rich and bold, the style and forms developed during this period reached a peak of refinement in the following decades.

WILLIAM & MARY

In 1688 Mary, daughter of James II, and her husband, Prince William of Orange, accepted the throne of England, bringing with them from Holland numerous craftsmen and quantities of baroque furniture. During their reign a style of furnishings emerged which was to be a transition between the elaborate forms of the Stuart period and the grace of the Queen Anne style.

Pieces distinctive of the period were china cabinets, round and oval gate-leg tables, banister-back chairs with crestings, higher bedsteads (some reached 16 feet), small tables for gaming, and the newly developed chest-on-frame (highboy) and dressing table (lowboy). Walnut was the most popular wood during this era.

Prominent characteristics of William and Mary furniture include turnings in the shape of the inverted cup (1), trumpet (2), gadrooning (3), perpendicular legs, the bun foot (4), the straight bracket foot (5), and the Spanish foot (6), with shaped stretchers often set crosswise between the legs (7).

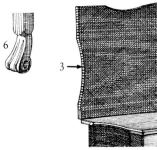

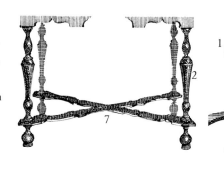

QUEEN ANNE

Queen Anne, second daughter of James II, ruled England from 1702 until 1714. The furniture style that bears her name, however, covers a period of forty years and includes the reign of George I and part of the reign of George II.

The style developed during this age of flourishing craftmanship is considered one of the most graceful of the century. Its most distinctive feature is an undulating line based on the "S" or cyma curve—an unbroken line with a convex and concave curve. William Hogarth, the celebrated eighteenth-century English painter and engraver, called this curve the "line of beauty."

The most fashionable wood was walnut, but mahogany was introduced about 1720. With the use of this wood furniture became lighter and more graceful; and elaborate carving, to which mahogany was especially suited, began to appear.

The Queen Anne chair is perhaps the most familiar design of the period. It has an extremely comfortable splat often shaped to fit the back. Card tables with turnover hinged tops, small tables, and lower chests of drawers were popular.

Characteristics of the Queen Anne style as interpreted in America were cabriole legs (1) with numerous forms of the foot: hoof (2), pad (3), trifid (4), and slipper (5). The claw-and-ball foot was also used during this time.

Other characteristics of this style are scroll tops on chests (6), and scalloped shells on knees of legs (7) and on crests of chairs (8).

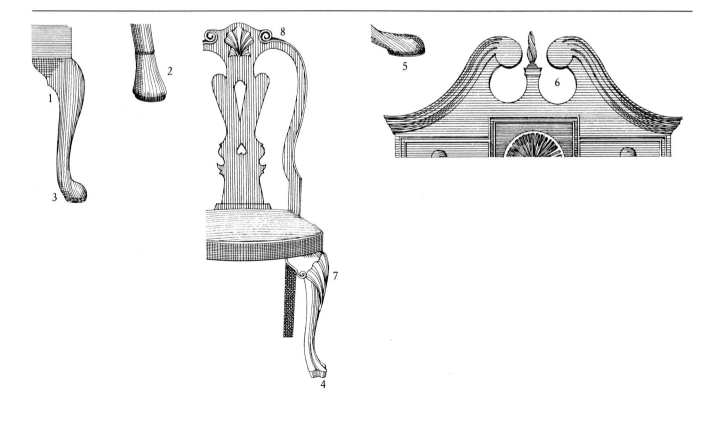

CHIPPENDALE

Thomas Chippendale, the best-known and best-advertised figure in the history of furniture-making, was born about 1705 and died in 1779. The first cabinetmaker to have his name associated with a furniture style, Chippendale was paradoxically a master of the derivative. Rarely inventive, he borrowed elements from Gothic, Chinese, and French designs and translated them into a new style.

Walnut and fruit woods, as well as mahogany, were widely used in America at this time, while English cabinetmakers preferred mahogany, an excellent wood for the crisp carving associated with Chippendale. Other popular Chippendale motifs included rococo or asymmetrical designs, simulated Chinese bamboo, the "C" scroll (1), and extensive use of fretwork.

The Chippendale straight leg, often terminating in a distinct Marlborough foot (2), was plain (3), fluted (4), carved (5), or decorated with applied frets (6). His cabriole leg was supported by the following types of feet: scroll or French toe (7), claw-and-ball (8), and hairy paw (9).

The ogee bracket foot (10) was often used on case pieces. Characteristic carved forms were the pierced or interlaced splat (11), tattered shell (12), acanthus leaf (13), drapery (14), and cabochon (15).

Many of his contemporaries were his equal as designer and craftsman; but in 1754 he published *The Gentleman and Cabinet-Maker's Director*, and this established him in the public mind as one of the foremost furniture designers of the period. Two later editions of the treatise were published, the last in 1762.

These publications are known to have reached America, and the style they delineated was adapted by American cabinetmakers to suit colonial tastes. For this reason many American-made pieces have wide variations from the original designs. For example, while the highboy or chest-on-frame went out of style in most parts of England in the mid-eighteenth century, it continued in America and was developed in the American Chippendale style to include the elegant Philadelphia chest-on-chest, the Boston Bombé type chest-on-chest, and the handsome Newport block front form. When we refer to "Chippendale" in this text, then, we are using the term in the American sense.

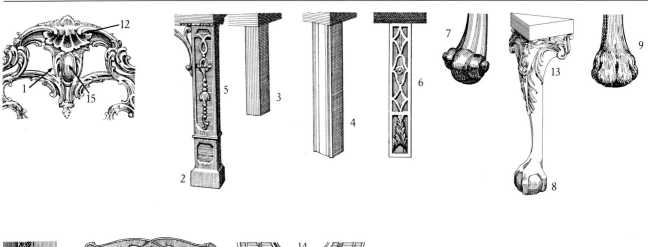

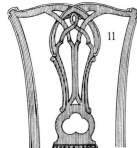
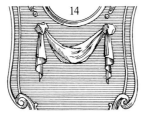

THE CLASSICAL REVIVAL

During the latter part of the eighteenth century Europe was swept by a wave of "classicism," inspired by renewed interest in Greek and Roman art and architecture.

In English furniture the classical revival meant the end of the elaborate, rococo Chippendale style and the introduction of the light, classical lines of Adam, Hepplewhite, and Sheraton.

Robert Adam, the best-known of three brothers, was among the first to popularize the new style in England.

Furniture in the Adam style was generally made of mahogany or satinwood, and cane-back pieces were popular. Slim tapered legs, often fluted (1,2), were distinguishing features of the style. The legs were square or round and usually supported by block or spade (3) feet.

Classical motifs in inlay or low relief carving were widely used; ornamental discs and ovals, spandrel fans, floral swags and pendants (4,5,6), and most importantly the classic urn (7).

George Hepplewhite was one of the many skilled craftsmen associated with the making of furniture to Adam's design. He was also important on his own as an interpreter of the classical in eighteenth-century English furniture.

Some distinguishing features of his designs include shield-shaped chair backs (8), heart-shaped backs (9), sheaves of wheat (10), carved drapery (11), bell flowers (12), prolific use of inlay, and painted designs decorating whole sets of furniture. Mahogany and satinwood were the popular woods.

American furniture of the Federal period was tremendously influenced by the design books of Thomas Sheraton, and his furniture enjoyed great popularity during an affluent period in America. The celebrated Duncan Phyfe was one of many American cabinetmakers who were influenced by the Sheraton style.

Sheraton used rectangular chair backs (13), rounded and tapered legs with reeding or fluting (14), diamond and lattice designs in chair backs (15), decorative motifs of swags, flowers, and drapery (16), spiral turnings (17), Prince of Wales feathers (18), and applied brass terminals (19).

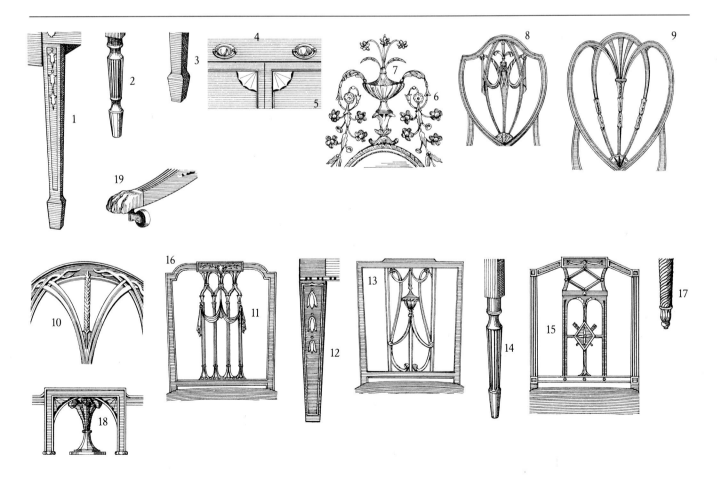

FURNITURE TERMS

APRON
A narrow strip of wood, adjoining the base of a cabinet carcase and extending between the tops of the legs or feet brackets. (As best represented by 39001; 39019; 39148; 38017; 38020).

BAIL HANDLE
A metal or wood handle curved upward at the ends (depending) from the sockets. (Represented by 39001; 39068; 38031).

BALUSTER
A small, slender turned column, usually swelled outward at some point between the base and the top. (Represented by 39070; 39049; 38009).

BAROQUE
An architectural style of Italian origin, characterized by conspicuous curves, scrolls, and highly ornate decoration.

BLOCK FOOT
A square, vertical-sided foot at the base of a straight, untapered leg. (Represented by 39170).

BOMBÉ
Outward swelling, curving or bulging. (Represented by 39176).

BRACKET FOOT
A protruding straight or ogee support. (Represented by 39068; 38008).

BUN FOOT
A flattened globed, or bun-shaped foot, with slender ankle above.

BURL
A swirled grain within wood which has been cut from a crotch or the stump of a tree. (Represented by 59005).

CABRIOLE
A springing curve. Term applied to legs that swell outward at the upper part, or knee, and inward at the lower part. (Represented by 39019; 39008; 38020).

"C" SCROLL
A carving in the shape of the letter "C". (Represented by 39067; 39142).

CARCASE OR CARCASS
A body of joinery, or cabinet work. (Represented by 39001; 39068; 39018).

CARTOUCHE
An ornamental form of irregular shape enclosing a plain central surface, often used as a field for painted devices or inscriptions.

CHAMFER
A beveled cutting away of a corner angle. (Represented by 39003; 39057; 39033; 38004).

COMPO
(short for composition) A mixture of resin and other materials for the fabrication or molding of relief for application. (Billiard balls are made of a mixture called compo). (Represented by 59003; 59006).

CRESTING
Ornamental topping, usually a chairback. (Represented by 39146).

CROSS BANDED
Wood which has been banded (cut) across the grain for molding or decorative purposes. (Represented by 39068; 39148; 59009).

CYMA CURVE
A wave curve; a double or compound curve. (Represented by 39151).

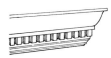

DENTIL
A form of molding ornamentation made by a set of oblong blocks set at equal distance from each other. (Represented by 39169).

DOVETAIL
Double fan, butterfly, or dovetail key block, fitted into conforming cuts in the surface of boards or planks to make a tightly fitted joint. (Represented by 39001; 39153; 39087; 39019; 38024).

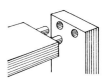

DOWEL
A wooden pin fastening two pieces of cabinet work together.

ESCUTCHEON
Keyhole cover of brass, silver, ivory, etc. (Represented by 39068; 39087; 38037).

FINIAL
A decorative finishing device for corners or projecting uprights. (Represented by 39092; 39058).

FLUTED
A series of grooves used to decorate columns or legs. (Represented by 39012).

FRET
Interlaced ornamental work, sometimes applied to solid background and sometimes perforated. (Represented by 39037; 39003; 39023; 38004).

GADROON
A carved or curved, fluted or ruffled, ornament for edges. (Represented by 39003).

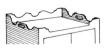

GALLERY
A raised rim of fretwork, or metal bar, surrounding tops of furniture (Represented by 39057).

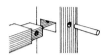

GREEK KEY
A border design of angular broken lines, repeated continuously. (Represented by 39158).

HOOF FOOT
Resembling a hoof.

INLAY
Where one wood is set into the body of another for decorative effect. (Represented by 39027; 39013; 39172; 39050).

JAPANNING
In earlier parlance, synonymous with lacquering. (Represented by 59007).

KNEE
The uppermost curve of a cabriole leg.

MASQUE
A full face (human, animal, or grotesque) used without the rest of the body, as a form of ornament.

MORTISE AND TENON
A method of joinery whereby one piece (tenon) is cut to precisely fit into another (mortise). Sometimes the tenon is further locked by means of a peg inserted through it.

OGEE
A form made by two opposite cyma curves, with their convex sides meeting in a point. (Represented by 39176).

PEDIMENT
An architectural cresting for large cabinet work, either triangular or scrolled. (Represented by 39158; 39169).

PENDANT
A hanging ornament.

ROCOCO
An elaborate form of ornamentation full of curves, shells, and other rustic details conventionalized. (Represented by 59006).

SKIRT
See Apron

SLIPPER FOOT
Usual on tripod legs and sometimes called snake foot. (Represented by 39005; 39149; 39182; 38009).

SPIRAL TURNING
A twisted form of turning frequently seen on legs and bed posts. (Represented by 39069).

SPLAT
The central member of a chair back. (Represented by 39142).

STRETCHER
The bracing between legs. (Represented by 39136).

TRIFID (OR DRAKE) FOOT
Usual on cabriole leg (like pad foot) which has been carved. (Represented by 39146).

WAINSCOT
Boards used for panel work. Panel work itself. (Represented by 39050).

WILLIAMSBURG FURNITURE
REPRODUCTIONS-ADAPTATIONS-INTERPRETATIONS

Williamsburg Furniture Reproductions are approved copies of eighteenth and early nineteenth century antiques owned by Colonial Williamsburg. Each reproduction is individually constructed and finished by Kittinger Company, Buffalo, N.Y. Primary woods used are generally of the finest South American mahogany. Secondary woods are like those used on the antiques. When veneers are required they are hand laid from careful selections of wood, as they would have been prepared when the original was made. Solid brass is hand filed to the same appearance of the colonial mounts. Kittinger's master craftsmen, following the traditions of the skilled artisans of the past make every attempt to make *Williamsburg* Reproduction Furniture the best available from any furniture manufacturer.

Williamsburg Furniture Adaptations are also made by Kittinger in Buffalo, New York. For a specific reason, the design or intended use is permitted to be altered. Changes, however, must follow the way in which the original cabinetmaker could have altered the piece. For instance, an arm chair adapted to match a reproduction side chair; a twin-size bed, as opposed to a double-size bed.

Williamsburg Adaptation Furniture Interpretations are generally modified in design and construction to conform to modern necessities of size, function, comfort, or possibly all three. While adhering to the basic principles of eighteenth century design, interpretations are intended for modern necessity of furnishing the smaller apartment, home or office. For instance, a coffee table by reducing the size of a "harvest" table, as coffee tables did not exist in the eighteenth century. Other changes permit storage in cabinets, partitions in drawers, changes in the heights of tables and chairs, or perhaps, the modifications of springs and upholstery. Most *Williamsburg* Interpretations, for all practical purposes, appear to be copies of original pieces. All conform to the very best traditional and modern manufacturing methods available to Kittinger Company.

The demanding requirements for *Williamsburg* Reproduction Adaptation, and Interpretation Furniture are rigorously supervised by the Products Review Committee in Colonial Williamsburg. All are available in a variety of approved finishes. The price list with this catalogue gives necessary specific information about fabric, yardage, down cushions and leather upholstery. Muslin prices of upholstered pieces include the cost of applying fabric provided by the purchaser. If you have questions write or call Craft House, Williamsburg, Virginia, 23185 (Telephone 804-229-1000).

A Kittinger master craftsman following the traditions of skilled artisans of the past.

This contemporary dining room features the 39033/39034 dining table with 39016 side chairs and 39116 arm chair. The painting is flanked by a pair of 39162 cellarettes. The accessories shown are 31032 pewter candlesticks, 24044 delft punch bowl and 24076 tobacco jars.

DINING ROOM TABLE 39033
(CW 33) & 39034 (CW 34)

This three-part dining room table illustrates the simplicity of line typical of the late Chippendale style. Diverse in its appearance and function, the table may be used in a variety of ways. The drop-leaf section alone is an excellent dining table for small parties; the two end sections locked together make a graceful round table or, used separately, they become console tables. When these three pieces are joined, a handsome long table is formed, accommodating 12 persons. The 114″ over-all length of the completed table is adjusted by dropping one or both leaves of the center section.

Below: Two end sections joined form a round table, 47″ in diameter. The drop-leaf center section will seat six people with top open, 67″ long.

39033 Center Section. Height 29¼″; width 48″; length: 22″ closed, 67″ open.

39034 End Section. Height 29¼″; width 48″; depth 23½″.

The original of this piece is English, late 18th century, Chippendale (George III).

DINING ROOM TABLE 39065
(CW 65) & 39066 (CW 66)
Another example of space-saving
beauty, this table offers center and end
sections which can be used together or
in combination with 24″ leaves to
create a good-size dining room table.
In limited space, two end sections
(39066) can be joined to make a
charming dining table in a small contemporary room; an end section used
alone is a handsome console table.
All sections are made with tilt tops
for use in a corner or against a wall.

Below: Two end sections, one center
section and two 24″ leaves, totaling
147″ in length.

39065 Center Section. Height 28½″;
length 32½″; width 48″.

39066 End Section. Height 28½″;
length 33¼″; width 48″.

The original of this piece is in the
Lightfoot House. English, circa 1770,
Chippendale, (George III).

In the room setting shown below two
39066 End Sections with one leaf
provide ample space for dining in style.
The table is set with the china pattern
Bianca and Williamsburg Shell sterling
silver flatware. The crystal is Teardrop
and the four brass candlesticks are
22210.

Also available with additional 24″ leaf
and support.

GATE-LEG TABLE 39117 (CW 117)
An elegant feature of this oval gate-leg table is the delicate shell and pendant design carved on the knee of each cabriole leg (see detail). When completely open, the table provides comfortable places for as many as eight persons. With both leaves down, the table becomes a narrow 24″—perfectly suited for today's smaller apartments.

Height 29″; width 58″; length: 24″ closed, 70″ open.

The original of this piece is English, circa 1730, Queen Anne (George III).

The view from this contemporary room provides a striking backdrop for the Queen Anne table (39117) with side chair (39146) and wing chair (39104) flanking it.

Detail of the hand-carved shell and pendant on the knee of the 39117 Table

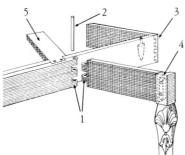

Construction features of 39117 Table: A wooden hinge (1) is held in place by a special pin (2). Apron rails are locked into sides with dovetail tenons (3). Mortise-and-tenon joint (4). Apron frame is braced diagonally for extra strength (5).

DROP-LEAF TABLE 38026 (WA 1026)
The drop-leaf table was popular in the colonies. The original, which inspired the 38026 table, was owned by Lucy Ludwell Paradise. Its dimensions have been slightly adjusted in the adaptation and two legs added for strength and stability.

38026 Drop-Leaf Table. Height 29½″; width 48″; length: 76″ open, 28″ closed.

The original of this piece is English, circa 1790, Hepplewhite (George III).

Right: The 38026 table when used alone is as versatile as the room or the occasion demands.

Below: Extra table space is obtained by the addition of two 38049 Console Ends at either end of the large table, for a total length of 124″.

CONSOLE END 38049 (WA 1049)
Below right: This Console End may be used as a handsome wall or hall table, or as an extension to either end of the 38026 Drop-Leaf Table.

38049 Console Ends.

Height 29½″; width 48″; depth 24″.

38026

38026

38049

19

SERVING TABLE 38069 (WA 1069)
This table is appropriate as a serving table, but could easily serve as either a writing or dressing table. Its simplicity of line, beautifully formed cabriole legs and accentuated pad foot all remind one of the original's Southern origin.

Height 29¼″; width 46″; depth 22″.

The original table is American, circa 1750, Queen Anne.

PEDESTAL DINING ROOM TABLE 38043 (WA 1043) & 38044 (WA 1044)
Inspired by an American antique in the furnishings of Colonial Williamsburg, this three-part dining room table is 108″ in length, accommodating 10 persons. Two end sections (38044) may be joined together (72″) for more compact dining; used separately an end section provides a pleasant console or serving table. Eighteen-inch leaves are available if the length needs to be further increased.

The dimensions of the original antique table have been reduced in the adaptation, and the angle of the legs changed for increased comfort and stability. Also, the drop leaves of the original end sections have been altered to the popular console form.

38043 Center Section. Height 29½″; width 46″; length 36″.

38044 End Section. Height 29½″; width 46″; length 36″.

The original of this piece is American, circa 1810-1820, Sheraton.

COFFEE TABLE 38033 (WA 1033)
Based on the design of an antique day bed made in Rhode Island, this adaptation has Queen Anne cabriole legs and finely turned stretchers. The table proportions are ample enough for use as a coffee table and for the display of objects.

Height 17¾"; length 46"; width 22½".

The original of this piece is American, circa 1730-1740, Queen Anne.

SERVING TABLE 39155 (CW 155)
This marble-topped table is supported by cabriole legs and trifid feet and is graced by delicate shell carvings on the apron and front knees. The marble surface makes it useful as a serving table and easy to maintain.

Height 27½"; length 52⅛"; depth 24".

The original of this piece is American, circa 1745, Queen Anne.

Detail of the shell carving on the apron of the 39155 Serving Table.

COFFEE TABLE 38042 (WA 1042)
An antique butler's tray was copied for the top of this mahogany table. It is fitted to a specially designed base shaped to the contour of the tray. Useful as a coffee or magazine table.

Height 21½″; width 27¾″; depth 21¾″.

The original of this piece is in the Moody House. English, late 18th century, Chippendale (George III).

TEA TABLE 38039 (WA 1039)
The original is in a Palace bedroom, painted black with an elegant Chinese lacquered tray top. The stretchers have the mark of Chippendale's style and insure sturdiness. It is very effective as an occasional table in mahogany or any authentic Williamsburg color.

Height 27½″; width 26″; depth 20⅜″.

Also available as a Coffee Table 38939.

Height 22½″; width 26″; depth 20⅜″.

The original of this piece is English, circa 1760, Chippendale (George III).

SERVING TABLE 38024 (WA 1024)
This adaptation serving table in mahogany is a size reduction of the antique. It is particularly useful for a small dining room. One of the drawers holds a sliding, removable silver tray.

Height 34¼″; length 47¾″; depth 20½″.

The original of this piece is in Christiana Campbell's Tavern. American, late 18th century, Hepplewhite.

DROP-LEAF COFFEE TABLE 38035 (WA 1035)

This 20th-century coffee table—a form unknown in the 18th century—has been adapted from a small drop-leaf table in the Williamsburg collection. The dimensions of the antique have been reduced in proper proportions to form a mahogany table of delightful simplicity.

Height 18¾″; width: 35″ open, 20⅛″ closed; length 42″.

The original of this piece is American, circa 1770, Chippendale.

Below: Table is shown with both leaves down.

TEA TABLE 39008 (CW 8)

A Massachusetts cabinetmaker designed the original of this elegant mahogany tea table. Like the antique, it is made of carefully selected mahogany with pine candle slides. Note the graceful scallops of the apron and the delicate hand carving of the cabriole legs.

Height 26¼″; length 29¾″; depth 18½″.

The original of this piece is American, circa 1735-1750, Queen Anne.

CARD TABLE 39003 (CW 3)

A Rhode Island cabinetmaker is believed to have made the original of this card table. The thumb-print molding on the flap-top edge and cavetto molding lighten the appearance of a double top. Throughout the entire piece, graceful Chippendale lines are faithfully copied in this mahogany reproduction.

Height 28¾″; length 30¼″; depth: 15¾″ closed, 31½″ open.

The original of this piece is in the Brush-Everard House. American, circa 1770, Chippendale.

CARD TABLE 39156 (CW 156)

This mahogany reproduction details the original's elaborate design of scroll shoulders and shell with pendant leaf. The claw-and-ball foot and the half-round design are attractive characteristics.

Height 28¾″; width 32¾″; depth: 32¼″ open, 16⅛″ closed.

The original of this piece is in the Peyton Randolph House. English, circa 1735, Chippendale (George I).

Detail of claw-and-ball foot on 39156 Table.

GAMING TABLE 39084 (CW 84)

Like its counterpart, this mahogany Pembroke gaming table has a top that slides and may be removed or turned. When removed, a hand-tooled leather backgammon board is revealed, and when reversed, there is a gaming board of inlaid wood for chess or checkers.

Height 28¼″; width 41½″ open, 23″ closed; depth 28″.

DROP-LEAF TABLE 38022 (WA 1022)
A handsome small dining table, this mahogany Queen Anne adaptation was inspired by an antique made in Virginia. As useful as it is handsome, it is only 16½″ wide when closed and fits conveniently against a wall. With the leaves open it provides a comfortable setting for three to four.

Height 29½″; length 42¾″; width: 43″ open, 16½″ closed.

The original of this piece is American, mid-18th century, Queen Anne.

TABLE 39309 (CW 309)
The Federal period was an era of change, not only in design but in mechanical innovation as well, and this folding card table demonstrates these new techniques. The acanthus carving of the central pedestal is based closely on ancient classical design. The clover-leaf top and brass lion-paw feet are innovative features of the new style. When the folding top is closed, the table sits flat against a wall; when open, the two side legs swing to the rear to provide support for the top.

Height 28⅞″; width 36″; depth: 18″ closed, 36″ open.

The original of this piece is American, circa 1815, Duncan Phyfe.

DROP-LEAF TABLE 38020 (WA 1020)
The Queen Anne styling of this elegant single drop-leaf table is seen in its graceful lines, cabriole legs, and pad feet. The original, made by a Massachusetts craftsman, is in the Colonial Williamsburg collection, and the adaptation differs from it only in unseen interior construction details.

Height 25¾″; length 31″; width: 23½″ open, 13½″ closed.

The original of this piece is American, circa 1730-1740, Queen Anne.

CORNER TABLE 39002 (CW 2)
The pad feet and graceful scalloped apron are particularly distinctive features of this Queen Anne table. Closed it fits snugly into small spaces, open it provides a two-foot-plus square surface.

Height 26¾″; diagonal width 35″; depth closed 18″; open 25″ x 25″.

The original of this piece is English, circa 1730, Queen Anne (George II).

DROP-LEAF TABLE 39167 (CW 167)
This six-sided gaming table, a copy of an English antique, has three gracefully indented corners on each leaf and tapered legs with capped knees and pad feet. With leaves extended, it seats four comfortably.

Height 28″; width 38¾″; length: 13¾″ closed, 45″ open.

The original of this piece is English, circa 1740, Queen Anne (George II).

TABLE 39160 (CW 160)
This copy of an antique drop-leaf "breakfast table" in the Williamsburg collection could serve for intimate dining in a small apartment or double as a card table. With leaves down, it becomes an attractive end table. The openwork stretchers of this mahogany table are illustrated in Chippendale's Directory of 1754.

Height 28½″; depth 30¼″; width: closed 20¼″, 40¾″ open.

The original of this piece is American, circa 1770, Chippendale.

CORNER TABLE 39172 (CW 172)
This unusual Queen Anne corner table has a triangular top with a serpentine front edge and a skirt which conforms to the shape of the top. There are holes in the sides of the table so that it can be secured to adjacent walls. The single cabriole leg terminates in a pad foot. The knee is outlined with carved "C" scrolls and is decorated with a carved shell and pendant bellflowers.

Height 30″; width 22¼″; depth 16″ at center.

The original of this piece is on the stair landing of the Peyton Randolph House. English, circa 1720, Queen Anne (George II).

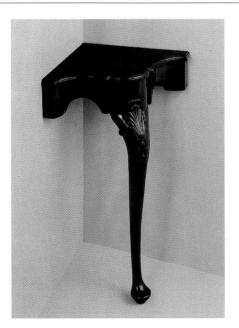

Detail of the carved shell and bellflowers on the knee of the 39172 Corner Table.

SQUARE TILT-TOP TABLE 39069 (CW 69)

Distinguished by a delicate tripod base and finely proportioned carved stem, this mahogany table is graceful yet unusually sturdy. As in all Williamsburg furniture, each part is carefully hand-joined.

Height 26¾"; top 25⅝" x 25⅝".

The original of this piece is in the Wythe House dining room. English, circa 1760, Chippendale (George III).

REVOLVING TILT-TOP TABLE 39011 (CW 11)

This intermediate-size mahogany table is a reproduction of a New England antique. An intricate bird-cage construction connects the revolving tilt-top to the base.

Height 27"; diameter 21½".

The original of this piece is in the parlor of the Lightfoot House. American, last quarter 18th century, Hepplewhite.

OVAL TILT-TOP TABLE 39135 (CW 135)

Characteristic of late 18th-century furniture, this oval table's tripod legs terminate in spade feet. The wood is mahogany.

Height 27½"; length 26"; width 17¾".

The original of this piece is in the Coke- Garrett House. American, late 18th century, Hepplewhite.

TILT-TOP TABLE 39070 (CW 70)
An unusual example of Chippendale design, this table has a bird-cage construction and claw-and-ball feet on curved legs. With a revolving tilt-top such pieces were frequently used as tea tables in the colonial period. Today it may serve a similar function, or it could even be used as a small table for dining.

Height 28¾"; diameter 34¾".

The original of this piece is in the Wythe House study. American, circa 1775, Chippendale.

TABLE 38066 (WA 1066)
This useful mahogany table is an adaptation from the original antique. It is also available with a square top (38009)

Height 27¼"; diameter 26¼".

The original of this piece is English, circa 1760-1775, Chippendale (George III).

TABLE 38009 (WA 1009)
This tripod table has been simplified in its adaptation from the original to create a sturdy mahogany occasional table.

Height 27¼"; top 25" x 25".

The original of this piece is in the Brush-Everard House. English, circa 1760-1775, Chippendale (George III).

PEMBROKE TABLE 38006 (WA 1006)
Classic Hepplewhite design has been
given a fresh look in this mahogany
Williamsburg adaptation by the use of
molding instead of inlay around the
drawer and leaves. The original table
is now used in the furnishings of
Colonial Williamsburg.

Height 28″; width: 39″ open, 20¾″
closed; depth 29¾″.

The original of this piece is American,
late 18th century, Hepplewhite.

PEMBROKE TABLE 39027 (CW 27)
According to tradition, tables of this
type were named for the Earl of
Pembroke. This Hepplewhite version
found great favor in the American
colonies and is distinguished by the
holly inlay on the legs and drawers,
the shape and thickness of the oval
top, and the size and taper of the legs.

Height 28¼″; width: 22″ closed, 46¾″
open; depth 33″.

The original of this piece is American,
late 18th century, Hepplewhite.

TABLE 38010 (WA 1010)
Today, as in the 18th century, circular tables are popular as small occasional or end tables. This mahogany Queen Anne table is an adaptation of the antique.

Height 26¾"; top diameter 20¼".

The original of this piece is in the parlor of the Wythe House. American, circa 1760, Queen Anne.

TABLE 38058 (WA 1058)
The practical size of this adaptation of an English provincial table permits a variety of uses. This single-drawer mahogany table has gracefully turned legs and feet.

Height 26⅜"; width 24"; depth 17".

The original of this piece is in the Great Room of Wetherburn's Tavern. English, first quarter 18th century, William and Mary.

TABLE 38029 (WA 1029)
This graceful mahogany table was inspired by an American antique now among the furnishings of a Williamsburg guest cottage. The slightly tapered legs and appealing proportions are exactly as those of the original. Useful as an occasional or end table, it also provides a good surface for a lamp or vase of flowers. The drawer is handy for small objects.

Height 29½"; width 25¼"; depth 18¾".

The original of this piece is American, late 18th century, Hepplewhite.

TABLE 39057 (CW 57)

This small table is a fine reproduction of an English antique. Notable Chippendale features are the scalloped gallery with pierced handholes, delicate leg brackets, and paneled doors. It is frequently used as a bedside table, but serves equally well next to a chair.

Height 31″; width 21″; depth 19¼″.

The original of this piece is in the Governor's Palace. English, mid-18th century, Chippendale (George III).

Detail of the leg brackets on the 39057 Table.

FLAP-TOP TABLE 39141 (CW 141)

This reproduction changes appearance as it does function: suitable as a serving table, a writing table, or a console. The rectangular folding top is supported on slender columnar legs terminating in turned feet. A delicate candleslide pulls out on either side; and two gates support the top when it is open.

Height 28½″; length 35¾″; depth: 12″ closed, 24″ open.

The original of this piece is in the Peyton Randolph House. English, circa 1720, Queen Anne (George I).

The versatile 39141 Table is shown with the delft brick 24026 and the Catesby print The Chatterer 14006.

**REVOLVING BOOK TABLE 39161
(CW 161)**
Eminently useful in library, den or office, and a conversation piece, too, this perfect reproduction keeps volumes close at hand. The hexagonal top, in swirl-figured mahogany, holds a lamp and knickknacks.

Height 29½"; top 25½" across flat sides.

The original of this piece is in the Peyton Randolph House. English, circa 1750, Chippendale (George II).

**PORRINGER TABLE 38057
(WA 1057)**
This handsome and useful table is adapted from an antique that was originally a tea or gaming table; it is typical of those made in New England. Candlesticks were placed on its porringer-shaped corners.

Height 26¾"; width 34"; depth 24".

The original of this piece is American, third quarter 18th century, Queen Anne.

TABLE 38004 (WA 1004)
Modeled on a Virginia Chippendale antique, this adaptation can be used as a dressing table, small desk, side or serving table.

Height 29½"; width 42"; depth 21".

The original of this piece is in the Wigmaker's Shop. American, circa 1750-1775, Chippendale.

TABLE 39311 (CW 311)
Inside the lower drawer of the original of this small, two-drawer table is the cabinetmaker's label. Made by Matthew Egerton, Jr. of New Brunswick, New Jersey, it was originally intended as a sewing or worktable, but today this mahogany reproduction would serve perfectly as a bedside table or small lamp table. The recessed front visually lightens the overall effect of the piece.

Height 28½"; width 19"; depth 14⅝".

The original of this piece is in the Coke-Garrett House. American, circa 1810, Hepplewhite.

TABLE 38059 (WA 1059)
The antique from which this versatile mahogany table was adapted was probably made in tidewater Virginia. Note the pattern caused by the joined top and the distinctive scribed outline of the drawer.

Height 27½"; width 28¾"; depth 18¼".

The original of this piece is in the Brush-Everard House. American, circa 1750, Queen Anne.

Detail of the hardware on the 38059 Table.

DRESSING TABLE 39145 (CW 145)
The original of this mahogany dressing table is a Philadelphia piece now in the Williamsburg collection. Both the hardware and details of the shell and leaf carving are very elegant. The cabriole legs terminate in fluted stockings and web feet. (See insets).

Height 28¼"; length 35"; depth 19½".

The original of this piece is in the Bracken House. American, mid-18th century, Queen Anne.

Details of the shell and leaf carving on the knee and the fluted stocking and web foot of the Table 39145

TABLE 38300 (WA 3000)
The utility of this small mahogany stand is enhanced by the drawer in the top, an unusual feature. Essentially designed in an earlier style, the thin band of inlay outlining the drawer indicates it was made about 1790. The original was made of cherry, probably in Connecticut.

Height 25⅝″; width 16¼″; depth 16⅛″.

The original of this piece is American, circa 1790, Hepplewhite.

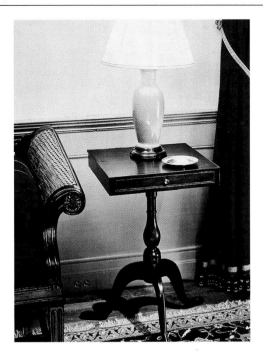

TABLE 38014 (WA 1014)
The straightforward simplicity of the antique is matched in this fine Chippendale table. Unlike the original, the mahogany adaptation is finished on the back so that it may be used as a free-standing table.

Height 28″; width 28¾″; depth 16″.

The original of this piece is English, circa 1760, Chippendale (George III).

TABLE 39318 (CW 318)
Card or gaming tables were popular forms of furniture in the Federal period. This copy of the Massachusetts original reveals most of the basic features of the Federal style: the elaborate use of cross-banded veneers and inlays, the lightness but strength of the overall construction, and the shaped reeded legs terminating in high, delicately-turned feet.

Height 30⅜″; width 37⅝″; depth 17⅝″ closed, 35¼″ open.

The original of this piece is in the Coke-Garrett House. American, circa 1810, Sheraton.

TABLE 39314 (CW 314)

Small tables or stands with folding tops were made in the Queen Anne and Chippendale periods, and this popularity continued unabated into the early years of the nineteenth century. The work of an unknown New York cabinetmaker, the clover-leaf top, classical urn pedestal, and flared, reeded legs of the original of this example indicate it was made about 1810.

Height 28½"; length 25"; width 17⅜".

The original of this piece is American, circa 1810, Sheraton.

NEST OF TABLES 39313 (CW 313)

Several new furniture forms were introduced during the Federal period. One of the most useful was the nest of tables. Ideal for use at parties and other social functions; when not in use, these tables can be stacked unobtrusively in a corner and still present an attractive appearance. Like the English originals, the tops of these faithful copies are made of highly-figured rosewood.

Height 29⅜" set; width 23¹/₁₆" set; depth 13" set.

The original tables are in the Coke-Garrett House. English, circa 1800, Empire.

DESK TABLE 39312 (CW 312)

Many pieces of Federal furniture can be used a variety of ways. Made in Baltimore by the noted cabinetmaker John Needle, the original of this piece was probably intended as a dressing table. Today it could serve its original purpose in a bedroom, or it could be used as a desk or as a small sideboard in a dining room. Each detail of the original has been faithfully copied.

Height 36⅝"; width 37¼"; depth 19½".

The original of this piece is in the Moody House. American, circa 1812, Hepplewhite.

Detail of the inlay on the 39312 Table.

SPIDER TABLE 39184 (CW 184)

An appealing mahogany drop-leaf table, which would be a welcome addition in any home. Its small size and six legs give this table a light, airy feeling that belies its actual sturdiness. It is called a "spider" table and the original can be seen in the upstairs hall of the Governor's Palace.

Height 27¾"; length 29"; width closed 11⅞"; width open 24¼".

The original of this piece is English, mid eighteenth century, Queen Anne.

TABLE 39316 (CW 316)

Small stands of this type are extremely versatile. With the top up they can be used to hold lamps, for serving drinks, and in many other ways. When not in use, the top can be folded down and the table placed against a wall where it takes up little space. This example, based on an original made in New York, is distinguished by a fluted classical urn at the base of its pedestal. The original is illustrated far right.

Height 26¾"; length 18½"; width 18¾".

The original of this piece is in the Coke-Garrett House. American, circa 1800, Sheraton.

The graceful shape of the top of the 39316 Table is readily apparent when folded down.

Lights and shadows delight the eye in this handsome contemporary room where the 38065 wing chair, the 39023 sofa, and the pair of 39128 side chairs are happily at home.

SIDE CHAIR 39128 (CW 128)
Reproduced in mahogany and covered in Wicker Velverette, this chair shows Georgian grace and dignity. The cabriole legs and pad feet are most attractive.

Height 38½″; width 23¼″; over-all depth 23″.

The original of this piece is English, circa 1740, Queen Anne (George II).

SIDE CHAIR 39067 (CW 67)
This chair is an elegant copy of an original George I side chair. The cabriole legs in front are decorated with a scalloped shell and bellflower motif finished in antique gold leaf.

Height 41½″; width 22¼″; over-all depth 24¼″.

The original of this piece is English, circa 1725, Queen Anne (George I).

Detail of the scalloped shell and bellflower on the leg of the 39067 Chair.

HIS LORDSHIP'S CHAIR 39013 (CW 13)

This high-backed Hepplewhite-style chair sometimes called the Martha Washington type, is an approved mahogany reproduction of an antique in the Williamsburg collection. The delicate inlay, tapering legs, and slender open arms are frequently seen in cabinetmakers' work of the late eighteenth century. The fabric is Multi-stripe.

Height 48″; width 26″; over-all depth 26½″; arm height 28″.

The original of this piece is American, circa 1790, Hepplewhite.

Detail of the inlay on the leg.

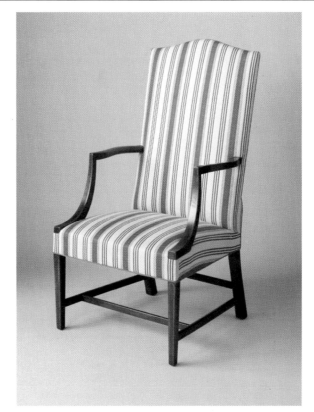

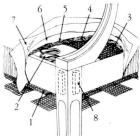

Construction features of 39013 Chair: Most Williamsburg upholstered pieces are constructed with webbing (1), springs (2), burlap (3), curled hair (4), cotton (5), muslin (6) and finally the cover (7). The seat rails are mortised and tenoned into the legs (8).

LADY'S CHAIR 38040 (WA 1040)

The handsome Chippendale chair shown here is covered in Potpourri. For added comfort, the back of this adaptation has been given more pitch and the seat more depth.

Height 41″; width 27½″; over-all depth 22¾″; arm height 24¾″.

The original of this piece is in the George Wythe House. American, circa 1760, Chippendale.

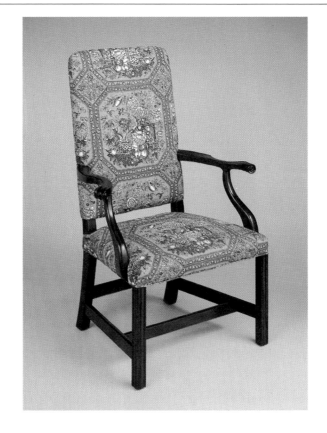

CHAIR 39307 (CW 307)
The term "Martha Washington" used to describe a chair of this design is a modern one, but it accurately reflects the period when graceful chairs like this one were first made. The high back, flowing lines, and an overall feeling of lightness and delicacy are hallmarks of the Federal style, which are superbly reflected in this copy of a Massachusetts chair made in about 1800.

Height 43⅝"; width 25⅞"; over-all depth 27"; arm height 26⅜".

The original of this piece is in the Coke-Garrett House. American, circa 1800, Hepplewhite.

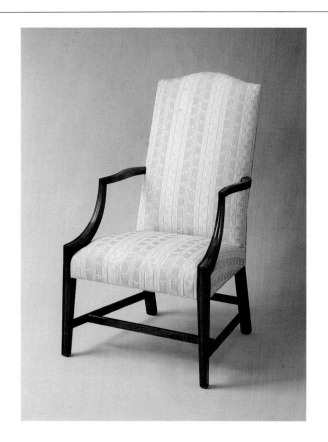

OPEN ARM CHAIR 39171 (CW 171)
The original chair is a fine American interpretation of Chippendale design. This handsome reproduction, shown here in Dobby Weave, is ideal for study or den.

Height 38"; width 24¼"; over-all depth 25¼"; arm height 26½".

The original of this piece is in the Peyton Randolph House. American, circa 1790, Chippendale.

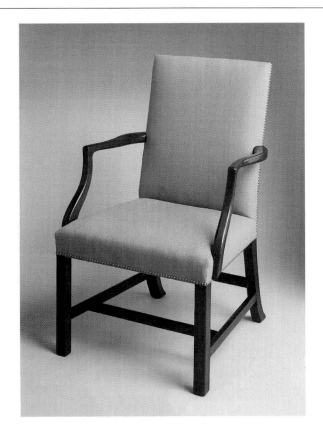

SIDE CHAIR 38046 (WA 1046)
OPEN ARM CHAIR 38056 (WA 1056)
The original of these fine mahogany
chairs was from a New England workshop. Both adaptations retain the
interesting crest rail and excellent
proportions of the original. The fabric
on the 38056 is Ludwell Damask.

38046 Side Chair. Height 37¾"; width
22¾"; over-all depth 23½".

38056 Open Arm Chair. Height 37¾";
width 24¾"; over-all depth 25½";
arm height 26".

The original of these pieces is American,
circa 1770, Chippendale.

38056

Simple and contemporary in feeling is
this combination of side chair and
table—particularly appropriate in
a hallway or entry area. The 38046
Side Chair (fabric, Liverpool Birds,
page 138) is paired with the 39160
Table, which provides the right surface
for the 35101 Tea Caddy. On the wall
is a hand-colored copy of the Nova
Virginia Tabular 58-601. Simplicity and
understatement often are keys to tasteful decorating.

38046

OPEN ARM CHAIR 38011 (WA 1011)
This small open arm chair was inspired by an American antique. It subtly modifies the original Chippendale lines by extra height and additional pitch to the back for enhanced comfort. It is shown here in Spotswood Damask.

Height 39″; width 24″; over-all depth 27¼″; arm height 24¾″.

The original of this piece is American, circa 1765-1770, Chippendale.

OPEN ARM CHAIR 38025 (WA 1025)
Based on an American antique, this fine Chippendale chair is often used in a study, den, or office. The adaptation has a deeper seat and boldly raked back for solid comfort. It is shown upholstered in Tulip.

Height 43½″; width 27¾″; over-all depth 27¼″; arm height 27¼″.

The original of this piece is in the study of the George Wythe House. American, circa 1770, Chippendale.

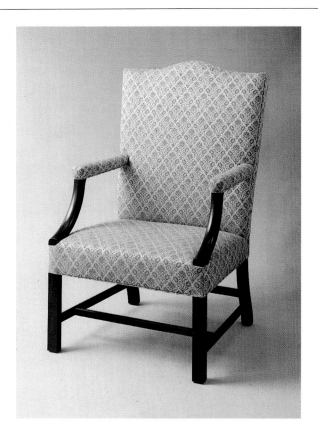

The 39668 partner's desk accompanied by 39152 open arm chairs and 39043 smoking chairs lend dignity as well as comfort to this distinguished office.

ARM CHAIR 39014 (CW 14)
Like the original, this reproduction is made of mahogany. Thomas Chippendale's style is apparent in the straight legs with delicate brackets, the graceful arms and the comfortably sloping back. Shown here upholstered in leather.

Height 38¾"; width 28¼"; over-all depth 29"; arm height 27".

The original of this piece is in the Governor's Palace, middle room. English, circa 1760, Chippendale (George II).

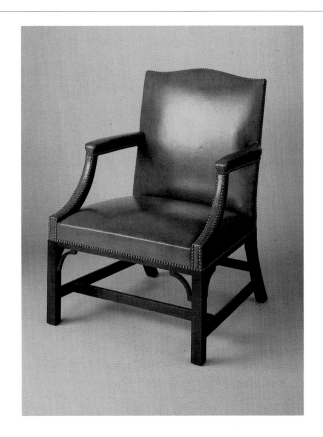

OPEN ARM CHAIR 39152 (CW 152)
Copied in precise detail from an antique in the Williamsburg collection, this unusual chair has been reproduced for use in homes and offices. It has square legs, rectangular stretchers, and simple curved arms.

Height 38½"; width 27"; over-all depth 27"; arm height 27½".

The original of this piece is English, circa 1765, Chippendale (George III).

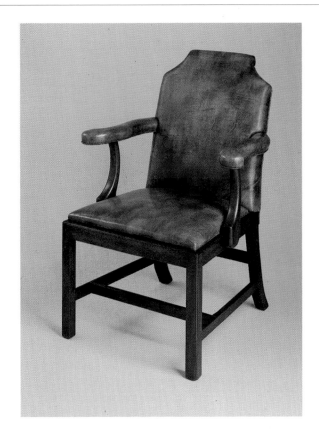

SMOKING CHAIR 39043 (CW 43)
The padded back and arm of this chair provide extra comfort for smoking or for sitting at a desk.

Height 34″; width 29″; over-all depth 24¼″; arm height 29½″.

The original of this piece is in the little middle room of the Governor's Palace. English, circa 1790, Chippendale (George III).

OPEN ARM CHAIR 39151 (CW 151)
A hand-carved and hand-finished copy, this chair has a solid, contoured back splat, cabriole legs and scroll arms—elegant and distinctive.

Height 39¾″; width 28″; over-all depth 23½″; arm height 27¼″.

The original of this piece is in the Lightfoot House. English, circa 1740, Queen Anne (George II).

SIDE CHAIR 39180 (CW 180)

This Queen Anne side chair is copied from one of a pair of English antiques in the Williamsburg collection. The curves in the serpentine cresting rail are repeated in the shape stiles that flank the broad, vase-shaped splat. A slip seat is supported on cabriole legs. The front legs terminate in claw-and-ball feet with curved hocks while the rear ones terminate in pads.

Height 38″; width 21⅞″; over-all depth 22½″.

The original of this piece is English, circa 1725, Queen Anne (George I).

Detail of the curved hock and claw-and-ball foot of the 39180 Chair.

SIDE CHAIR 39146 (CW 146)

The original of this Queen Anne chair was made in Philadelphia. It is fairly elaborate in design and details, with "cone and heart" piercing in the splat, a serpentine crest rail with scallop shell and additional carving of the knee and leg—particularly appropriate as a dining room chair.

Height 43¼″; width 20¼″; over-all depth 20″.

The original of this piece is American, circa 1735, Queen Anne.

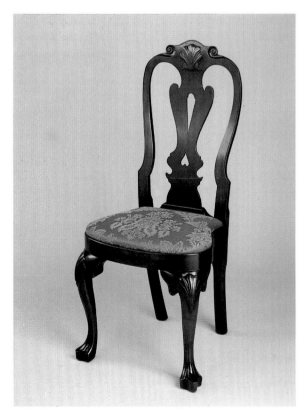

Detail of the hand-carved leg of the 39146 Chair.

47

SIDE CHAIR 38070 (WA 1070)
The strong character of this mahogany chair is enforced by the delicately purfled splat and Marlborough legs. Used by itself or in a set, this chair is an elegant addition to your home or office. Also available with upholstered seat (38970).

Height 38″; width 21″;
over-all depth 20¼″.

The original of this piece is in the Raleigh Tavern. American, circa 1760-1780, Chippendale (George III).

ARM CHAIR 38170 (WA 1070½)
The arms have been added to this version of the 38070 for greater versatility. It can be used with the side chairs to create a traditional set of chairs. Also available with upholstered seat (38670).

Height 38″; width 26½″; over-all depth 21¼″; arm height 27″.

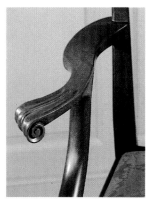

SIDE CHAIR 38018 (WA 1018)
& ARM CHAIR 38118 (WA 1118)
This mahogany adaptation of a
Chippendale side chair made in Virginia
(between 1760 and 1780) borrowed the
antique's sturdy construction and
simple pierced back splat. Arms for the
arm chair were designed from another
Chippendale model of the same
period. They have slip seats, but are
also available with upholstered seats
38048 and 38148.

38018 Side Chair with slip seat and
38048 Side Chair with upholstered
seat. Height 37½"; width 21"; over-all
depth 20".

38118 Arm Chair with slip seat and
38148 Arm Chair with upholstered
seat. Height 37½"; width 25"; over-all
depth 21¼"; arm height 27¼".

The original of these pieces is in the
Brush-Everard House. American, circa
1770, Chippendale.

38048

38018

38148

38118

SIDE CHAIR 39016 (CW 16)
This mahogany Chippendale straight chair is of simple design, except for the pierced or interlaced back splat. It is both sturdy and comfortable.

Height 37¼"; width 22"; over-all depth 21½".

The original of this piece is English, circa 1765, Chippendale (George III).

ARM CHAIR 39916 (CW 16½)
The addition of arms to the 39016 illustrates the adaptability of high quality eighteenth century design.

Height 37¼"; width 24"; over-all depth 21½"; arm height 27⅝".

The original is English, circa 1765, Chippendale.

Detail of the carving on the 39016 and 39916 Chairs.

SIDE CHAIR 38019 (WA 1019)
& ARM CHAIR 38119 (WA 1119)
These two stylishly simple Queen
Anne chairs were copied from antiques
in the Williamsburg collection. For
greater comfort, the adaptations have
upholstered rather than slip seats.
Those pictured here are covered in
leather.

38019 Side Chair. Height 38″; width
21¼″; over-all depth 21½″.

38119 Arm Chair. Height 38″; width
26″; over-all depth 23½″; arm height,
28¼″.

The originals of these pieces are English,
second quarter 18th century, Queen
Anne (George II).

CHAIR 39017 (CW 17)
Made in Philadelphia, the original of
this chair is an example of Chippendale
simplicity. This reproduction is covered
in leather.

Height 37½″; width 22½″; over-all
depth 23¾″.

ARM CHAIR 39917 (CW 17½)
This armchair version of 39017 can be
used as a pair at either end of a dining
table along with other 39017 chairs on
the sides. It is solid mahogany.

Height 37½″; width 25″; over-all
depth 24½″; arm height 26¾″.

The original of these pieces is American,
late 18th century, Chippendale.

CHAIR 38608 (WA 3008)
One of the features of the later Federal
style was a reliance on architecturally
correct copies of ancient Greek and
Roman furniture. The English maker
who crafted this graceful armchair
copied almost literally the design of an
ancient Greek Klismos chair, but he
updated it by painting it green and
caning the seat and back. The running
Greek key design on the front seat rail
further underscores the reliance of the
makers of Federal furniture on classical
motifs.

Height 33″; width 21⅞″; over-all depth
22⅝″.

The original of this piece is English,
circa 1800, Early Empire.

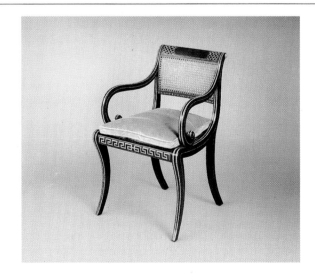

SIDE CHAIR 39142 (CW 142)
The original of this chair is one of a
set of six in the Colonial Williamsburg
collection. For comfortable dining, the
back splat was contoured. Particularly
noteworthy is the graceful scroll
carving flanking the knees.

Height 40½"; width 21¼"; over-all
depth 20½".

The original of this piece is English,
circa 1740, Queen Anne (George II).

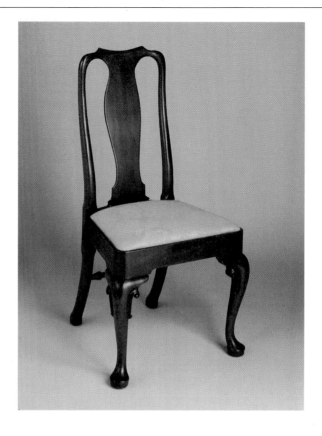

ARM CHAIR 39942 (CW 142½)
Graced by the same fine features as
39142, this chair has the addition of
arms and handsomely heads a table
surrounded by the side chairs.

Height 40½"; width 24"; over-all
depth 22¾"; arm height 27½".

The original of this piece is English,
circa 1740, Queen Anne (George II).

Detail of the hand-carved
scroll on the knee of the
39142 Side Chair and 39942
Arm Chair.

ARM CHAIR 39047 (CW 47)
& SIDE CHAIR 39947 (CW 47½)
Meticulously copied from the originals, these chairs can be used in combination at a dining table or singly at a desk. The back splats are elegantly interlaced. The examples shown are covered in Ludwell Adaptation Damask.

39047 Arm Chair. Height 37¾"; width 26"; over-all depth 22½"; arm height 27".

39947 Side Chair. Height 37¾"; width 22¼"; over-all depth 22".

The originals of these pieces are English, circa 1765, Chippendale (George III).

39047

39947

Detail of the arm of the 39047 Arm Chair.

CORNER CHAIR 39136 (CW 136)
The original of this chair was constructed in Philadelphia. It is an occasional, corner or desk chair, often called a "roundabout chair," and demonstrates the cabinetmaker's art.

Height 31¼"; width 26"; over-all depth 26"; arm height 29¾".

The original of this piece is American, circa 1750-1775, Chippendale.

WING CHAIR 39012 (CW 12)
Made by a Rhode Island craftsman, the original of this chair is now in the Williamsburg collection. The otherwise severe legs are stop-fluted and the chair has a sturdy appearance that makes it a natural for a study, den, or club. The chair is covered in Grapes.

Height 45½"; width 31"; over-all depth 28"; arm height 25½".

The original of this piece is American, third quarter 18th century, Chippendale.

BARREL CHAIR 39666 (CW 166A)
This reproduction is at home in any room: cozy, comfortable and pleasing. Its cabriole front legs end in high pad feet and the flaring rear legs are square.

Height 40"; width 28"; over-all depth 29½"; arm height 25¼".

The original of this piece is English, circa 1750, Queen Anne (George II).

WING CHAIR 38047 (WA 1047)
Elegance and comfort are combined in this adaptation of an English antique in the Williamsburg collection. The wings and beautifully proportioned rolled arms are carefully copied. The front legs are somewhat more tapered for great lightness in feeling and the chair has been lowered slightly.

Height 45″; over-all width 29″; over-all depth 28″; arm height 27½″.

The original of this piece is in the Powell-Waller House. English, circa 1790, Hepplewhite (George III).

WING CHAIR 38065 (WA 1065)
Graceful lines and mahogany cabriole legs distinguish this adaptation wing chair.

Height 44½″; width 28½″; over-all depth 31″; arm height 26¼″.

The original of this piece is in the Ewing House. English, circa 1720, Queen Anne (George I).

WING CHAIR 39163 (CW 163)

This timeless piece enters into any setting with magnificent effect. The front legs are cabriole with disc feet and the rear ones S-shaped.

Height 49"; width 32½"; over-all depth 32¼"; arm height 26¼".

The original of this piece is English, circa 1720, Queen Anne (George I).

Detail of the hand-carved leg of the 39163 Chair.

WING CHAIR 39044 (CW 44)

The original of this graceful and comfortable chair is in the Williamsburg collection. The reproduction, in mahogany, is a true copy. Particularly noteworthy are the cabriole legs with beautifully turned stretchers. These chairs fit into formal or informal settings alike. The fabric depicted here is Jones Toile.

Height 46"; width 36¾"; over-all depth 33½"; arm height 25½".

The original of this piece is American, circa 1750, Queen Anne.

WING CHAIR 38012 (WA 1012)
This adaptation has the same fine bow
in the upper wing as the original chair,
but has a thicker cushion for extra
comfort. It is shown here in leather.

Height 45″; width 32″; over-all depth
32″; arm height 24″.

The original of this piece is American,
circa 1775-1780, Chippendale.

WING CHAIR 39104 (CW 104)
Sturdiness, comfort and elegance
were often distinguishing marks of
Chippendale, and this approved reproduction captures these qualities. The
original chair is now in the furnishings
of Colonial Williamsburg.

Height 44″; width 33″; over-all depth
31½″; arm height 26″.

The original of this piece is English,
circa 1745, Chippendale (George II).

Detail of the hand-carved leg
on 39104 Chair, showing
acanthus leaves and ball-and-
claw foot.

CHAIR 39305 (CW 305)

Few easy chairs were made in the Federal period, as the form was almost out of fashion by the end of the eighteenth century. The Baltimore cabinetmaker, who made the original from which this copy is derived, admirably succeeded in lightening the essentially heavy lines of the form by banding the skirt of the front and sides in mahogany and inlaying the tapering front legs with boxwood husks.

Height 44½"; width 31¾"; over-all depth 33"; arm height 26½".

The original of this piece is in the Moody House. American, circa 1800, Hepplewhite.

Detail of the inlay on the leg of the 39305 Chair.

CHAIR 39304 (CW 304)

This is an unusual but extremely useful chair. It retains the clean, straight lines of Martha Washington type chairs, such as 39307, and also incorporates padded and rolled arms, such as those on easy chair 39305, for added comfort. The original was made in New England about 1800.

Height 44¼"; width 28¼"; over-all depth 26½"; arm height 25".

The original of this piece is in the Moody House. American, circa 1800, Hepplewhite.

BENCH 39147 (CW 147)

The perfect occasional seat, now as in the 18th century, has been faithfully reproduced in solid mahogany. The fabric is Green Spring Damask.

Height 17"; length 17"; width 21½".

The original of this piece is in the James Anderson House. English, circa 1740, Queen Anne (George II).

BENCH 39185 (CW 185)
This charming bench with a curving front serves perfectly as a window seat as well as an extra seat wherever needed. The fabric is Tulip.

Height 17½"; length 32⅝"; width 14⅛".

The original of this piece is English, circa 1790, Hepplewhite (George III).

BENCH 38016 (WA 1016)
A copy of an English antique in the Williamsburg collection. Practical as an extra seat or as a dressing table bench. Here shown covered in 29203 Bargello Flame stitch.

Height 16¾"; width 19¾"; depth 15¾".

The original of this piece is English, circa 1760, Chippendale (George III).

59

The 39034 table, 39151 arm chair, 38020 drop-leaf table, and the 39154 settee are perfect additions to this gracious contemporary setting.

SETTEE 39154 (CW 154)

An elegant Queen Anne settee in mahogany, from an original made in England. Its basically simple construction is complemented by skillful details in the woodwork; the cabriole legs have scroll-like wings and pad feet, while the outcurving arms terminate in graceful volutes. The fabric shown here is Bruton Adaptation Damask.

Height 36¾"; length 53¾"; over-all depth 29¼"; arm height 25¾".

The original of this piece is in the Brush-Everard House. English, circa 1725, Queen Anne (George I).

Detail of the spiral turn of the arm.

SOFA 39301 (CW 301)

The Massachusetts craftsman who made the original from which this copy is derived was obviously familiar with Thomas Sheraton's classic design, as evidenced by the turned, vase-shaped arm supports and the tapering reeded legs. Here shown upholstered in Bruton Damask.

Height 34½"; length 68"; over-all depth 28½".

The original of this piece is American, circa 1810, Sheraton.

SOFA 39303 (CW 303)

The compact proportions of this sofa greatly enhance its usefulness. Unusual features are the inlaid panels of bird's-eye maple on the back crest rail. This reproduction is a faithful duplication of the original Massachusetts piece. The fabric is Bluebell Stripe.

Height 34⅜"; length 60⅛"; over-all depth 23¾"; arm height 28⅜".

The original of this piece is in the Coke-Garrett House. American, circa 1810, Sheraton.

SOFA 39023 (CW 23)

Oriental motifs were popular in the late 18th century, and the front legs of this Chippendale sofa, following its original, have a Chinese fretwork design. This piece achieves distinction in its classic flowing lines in back and arms. It is shown upholstered in Herringbone Strie.

Height 35½″; over-all length 73″; over-all depth 31½″; arm height 30″.

The original is English, circa 1770, Chippendale (George III).

Detail of hand-carved leg on 39023 Sofa.

SOFA 39118 (CW 118)

For an unusually large private or public room, this handsome reproduction faithfully copies the unusual length and sweeping back of the antique. Here shown upholstered in Tulip.

Height 35¾″; over-all length 91″; over-all depth 30″; arm height 28¾″.

The original of this piece is in the King's Arms Tavern. English, circa 1770-1790, Chippendale (George III).

SOFA 39129 (CW 129)

This beautiful mahogany sofa, copied from an English antique, is distinguished by its flowing lines and ample proportions. Comfortable and practical, it seats three persons with ease.

Height 36″; length 79″; over-all depth 30½″; arm height 30¾″.

The original of this piece is in the Lightfoot House. English, circa 1760-1775, Chippendale (George III).

SOFA 39174 (CW 174)

This sofa with serpentine cresting and front seat rail, rolled arms, and four cabriole front legs with claw-and-ball feet is copied from an English antique. The original piece was owned by a person in Newburyport, Mass., during the eighteenth century. This history is of importance, for it further documents the use of high-styled English furniture in American homes from an early date.

Height 35⅞″; length 88½″; over-all depth 33¼″; arm height 31″.

The original of this piece is English, circa 1760, Chippendale (George III).

Detail of the hand-carved leg and claw-and-ball foot of the 39174 Sofa.

LOVE SEAT 38055 (WA 1055)
A smaller version of the 38005 sofa,
this upholstered mahogany love seat
would go in a conversation nook,
entrance hall, or bedroom, or could
serve as an additional piece in a fair-
sized living room. It is illustrated here
in leather.

Height 36¼"; over-all length 61"; over-
all depth 32½"; arm height 30½".

The original of this piece is American,
circa 1770, Chippendale.

SOFA 38005 (WA 1005)
The unmistakable lines of the original
Chippendale antique are matched in
this adaptation. This is the hump-
backed silhouette, with lines flowing
into the graceful arms. The sofa provides comfortable seating for three.
The fabric shown is Jones Toile.

Height 36¼"; over-all length 84";
over-all depth 32½"; arm height 30½".

The original of this piece is American,
circa 1770, Chippendale.

The 38060 chest provides ample storage in this inviting foyer.

SIDEBOARD 39300 (CW 300)

The original of this finely detailed sideboard was made in South Carolina. Of conventional form, the piece is distinguished by a virtual vocabulary of classically inspired inlaid motifs—husks, flutes, paterae—each meticulously done in holly against a figured mahogany ground.

Height 36″; length 72″; depth 27⅝″.

The original of this piece is in the dining room of the Coke-Garrett House. American, circa 1800, Hepplewhite.

SIDEBOARD 39148 (CW 148)

A reproduction of an English antique, this low sideboard is equally at home in a hallway or dining room. Note the carved apron, paneled sides, cross-banded mahogany encircling the drawers, and the unusual brasswork.

Height 33¾″; length 77½″; depth 21¼″.

The original of this piece is English, circa 1740, Queen Anne (George II).

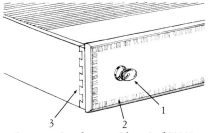

Construction features (above) of 39148 Sideboard: Custom-made oval brass knobs with nickel silver insert through center (1). Cross-banded border of mahogany (2). Dovetail tenons (3).

SIDEBOARD 39087 (CW 87)

Reproduced from an antique, this compact mahogany sideboard has four finely tapered square legs in front and two in the rear. Octagonal key escutcheons and heavy round brass knobs add distinctiveness to a simple and classic design.

Height 40½″; length 57″; depth 20¼″.

The original of this piece is in Christiana Campbell's Tavern. American, late 18th or early 19th century, Hepplewhite.

SIDEBOARD 38017 (WA 1017-1)

A low cupboard in the Chippendale style, now in the Williamsburg collection, inspired this unusual sideboard of fine mahogany fitted with brass escutcheons and H-hinges. For modern living, the original has been scaled down and fitted inside with two silver storage drawers and six adjustable shelves. The middle compartment opens for additional storage space.

Height 36″; length 66″; depth 20¾″.

The original of this piece is American, last half 18th century, transitional Chippendale-Hepplewhite.

SIDEBOARD 38041 (WA 1041)

An elegant accessory for the small dining room, this Hepplewhite sideboard was copied from an American antique now in Williamsburg. The two cabinets can be locked and the top drawer is partitioned and lined for silver flatware. The drawers have traditional brass fittings.

Height 39¾"; length 56½"; depth 24".

The original of this piece is in the Christiana Campbell's Tavern. American, circa 1800, Hepplewhite.

CELLARETTE 39162 (CW 162)

This handsome cellarette is an exact copy of an American antique. The top compartment provides ample storage space for bottles and the lower section has a convenient drawer for necessary bar equipment and a handy sliding shelf for service. Both sections may be locked.

Height 40¾"; width 25¼"; depth 15½".

Inside cellarette compartment; Height 11¾"; width 22"; depth 12⅞".

The original of this piece is in the Coke-Garrett House. American, circa 1790, Hepplewhite.

CABINET 39186 (CW 186)

The original metal lined cabinet is a platewarmer. This mahogany adaptation cabinet is identical to the original except for the deletion of the interior metal lining. The two adjustable shelves will accommodate a small television or serve as a bar. Its height and side flaps also make it usable as a lectern.

Height 36⅞″ open, 37⅝″ closed; width 37¼″ open, 18⅝″ closed; depth 19⅜″.

COLLECTOR'S CHEST 38068 (WA 1068)
SILVER CHEST 38968 (WA 1068-1)

A fine English chest on frame in the Chippendale style, circa 1770, now displayed at the Governor's Palace, has been superbly made to create a collector's or silver chest of rare elegance. Candle slides and polished brass pulls accent the graceful lines of this distinctive piece. Its small size makes it appropriate for use in any space where the scale calls for a delicate touch. The silver chest is lined with Pacific cloth.

Height 35⅞″; width 24⅞″; depth 12⅝″.

DESK 38964 (WA 1064½)
The narrow width and graceful form
of this mahogany slant-top desk
permits its use in any setting. When
open, three drawers and seven convenient pockets appear. Shown below
with the bookcase top.

Height 41″; width 39⅝″; depth 21¾″.

BOOKCASE DESK 38064 (WA 1064)
A Southern antique from about 1770
inspired this tall bookcase desk with
its handsome panelled doors and
bracket feet. The bookcase section
contains three adjustable shelves.
(Also available without the bookcase.
See above.)

Height 81½″; width 40½″; depth 21¾″.

The original of this piece is now in the
Students Room of the George Wythe
House. American, circa 1770,
Chippendale.

DESK 39901 (CW 1½)
This slant-top desk opens to disclose nine small drawers and four letters pockets. With a bookcase unit on top, it becomes the 39001 Secretary Desk, which is shown below with additional information.

Height 40″; width 41½″; depth 20½″.

Detail of the shell carving in the apron of the 39001 Secretary Desk and 39901 Desk.

SECRETARY DESK 39001 (CW 1)
The slant-top secretary is a fine reproduction of an historic antique made in New England. Elegant and serviceable, there are several drawers and pockets on the desk level, and a bookcase unit on top. (Without the bookcase, the desk is 39901 above.) The four large lower drawers and the lid are furnished with highly decorative brasses. The apron, too, is quite elaborate on both front and sides, and carries a shell carving (see detail above).

Height 61″; width 41½″; depth 20½″.

The original of this piece is American, circa 1770, Chippendale.

Construction features of the 39001 Secretary Desk: Six dovetail tenons (1) hold upper case (2) secure by locking top to ends at pediment (3).

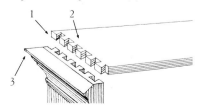

SLANT-TOP DESK 39969 (CW 169½)
This desk is the same as the one used for the 39169 Secretary, but it does not have the bookcase on top. Where space is limited, this piece of furniture provides a useful writing area and storage space.

Height 42⅞"; width 44¼"; depth 23".

The original of this piece is American, late 18th century, Chippendale.

SECRETARY BOOKCASE 39169
(CW 169)
The original of this piece is believed to have been made in Virginia during the last quarter of the eighteenth century. While the antique is of walnut, this secretary has been reproduced in the finest solid mahogany and mahogany veneer. Behind the glass doors on the upper section there are three shelves, two of which are adjustable. The slant-top desk folds out for a writing surface, and there are four graduated drawers below for storage space. All doors and drawers have locks.

Height 99⅝"; width 44¼"; depth 23".

The original of this piece is American, late 18th century, Chippendale.

Detail of the pediment of the 39169 secretary.

DESK 38037 (WA 1037)
This desk was copied from an English Chippendale piece; both the desk and frame match the lines and spirit of the antique. In the adaptation, the leather writing-surface is replaced by mahogany. The lid and the two lower drawers have fine brasses.

Height 38″; width 26½″; depth 21″; height of writing surface 29″.

The original of this piece is in the Lightfoot House. English, circa 1770, Chippendale (George III).

PARTNER'S DESK 39168 (CW 168)
This is a double desk, copied from an antique in the Colonial Williamsburg collection, with nine drawers identically placed front and back. It is also sectional, with the two pedestals separate from the top. The ormolu handles are

of cast brass. Modesty panel optional. Available in two lengths.

39168. Height 31″; length 58¾″; width 40¼″.

39668. Height 31″; length 68¾″; width 40¼″.

The original of this piece is in the Governor's Palace dining room. English, circa 1765, Chippendale (George III).

An impressive piece, the 39168 Partner's Desk lends great dignity to a professional man's office. In a home, this desk distinguishes a library or study, and its double drawer space (front and back), allows husband and wife to have separate storage areas. The open arm chair 39171 is in the foreground, and the 39164 Bookcase and 39012 Wing Chair are in the background.

This boardroom commands your attention with the 38043/38044 pedestal table, 39152 chairs and 39158 breakfront.

BREAKFRONT BOOKCASE 39158
(CW 158)

This stunning reproduction in solid mahogany and selected mahogany veneer matches in every detail its antique prototype. It is also related to bookcases illustrated in Chippendale's *Gentleman and Cabinet-Makers' Director*. Like the original, it is made in sections —cornice, cabinet and base—for greater ease in moving. Three drawers are 'hidden' in the Greek key design atop the base section. Striking brasswork, adjustable shelves, and locking cabinets and drawers complete this beautiful display piece.

Height 95⅞"; width 71½"; depth 18¾".

The original of this piece is English, circa 1750, Chippendale (George II).

BREAKFRONT 39302 (CW 302)

The basic design of this winged breakfront is closely related to similar pieces
made during the Chippendale period.
However, the unknown Boston cabinetmaker who executed the original has
lightened the overall effect by a sparing
use of wood. The influence of the
Gothic Revival, which was introduced
during the Federal period, can be seen
in the pointed arches at the top of
each door. Each compartment of the
top section has one stationary and
three adjustable shelves.

Height 87¼''; length 61¾''; depth 17⅜''.

The original of this piece is in the
Moody House. American, circa 1810,
Hepplewhite.

BOOKCASE 39164 (CW 164)

This mahogany piece is a handsome and versatile reproduction. Shelves are adjustable to display objets d' art and fine books, and it has a capacious full-width drawer in the base. Its intermediate size would recommend it as a useful and tasteful addition to library, study, office or executive suite. It has full locks on cabinet and drawer.

Height 79½″; width 46¾″; depth 15¾″.

The original of this piece is in the Peyton Randolph Office. English, circa 1740, Chippendale (George II).

CHEST 39018 (CW 18)

The original of this piece is an antique mahogany chest of drawers now used in Colonial Williamsburg. This meticulous reproduction has graduated drawers, bracket feet, reeded quarter-round columns, and striking brass lock fixtures and drawer pulls.

Height 35½″; width 38¼″; depth 19½″.

The original of this piece is in the George Wythe House. American, circa 1770, Chippendale.

Construction features of 39018 Chest: Drawer runners (or dust panels) are tenoned into ends (1). Drawers are dovetailed front (2) and back (not shown). Cock bead is around each drawer (3). Custom hardware is used (4). Fluted quarter-round column pilasters cover complex joinery of chest frame (5).

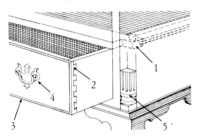

CHEST 38060 (WA 1060)

The paneled ends, simple brass drawer pulls, and joined top gives this handsome mahogany chest an air of quiet distinction. It would be equally at home in a bedroom, living room or hallway. There are locks in four drawers.

Height 31⅞″; length 52½″; depth 20⅞″.

The original of this piece is in the George Wythe House. American, circa 1740-90, Chippendale.

CHEST OF DRAWERS 38002
(WA 1002)
A Virginia antique was adapted to
make this medium-sized Chippendale
chest of drawers. Like the original, the
mahogany adaptation has clean lines
and simple but effective brasswork.

Height 35¼″; width 37½″; depth 21¾″.

The original of this piece is American,
circa 1775, Chippendale.

CHEST OF DRAWERS 38008
(WA 1008)
A Virginia-made antique was the
inspiration for this mahogany Chippendale chest. It follows a colonial tradition
of simplicity combined with gracious
proportions: a bracket base, with
subtly graduated drawer size, and
simple but effective brasswork.

Height 46¼″; width 40″; ; depth 20″.

The original of this piece is in Market
Square Tavern. American, circa 1770,
Chippendale.

CHEST 39176 (CW 176)

The design and details of this mahogany chest make it a most attractive reproduction of the original Pennsylvania piece. The top surface conforms to the serpentine shape of the front, and the handcarved fretwork embellishes the chamfered corners. Graduated drawers are generous in size, and each one has a lock.

Height 33½"; width 44¼"; depth 23".

The original of this piece is American, circa 1770, Chippendale.

Detail of the handcarved fretwork on the corners of the 39176 Chest.

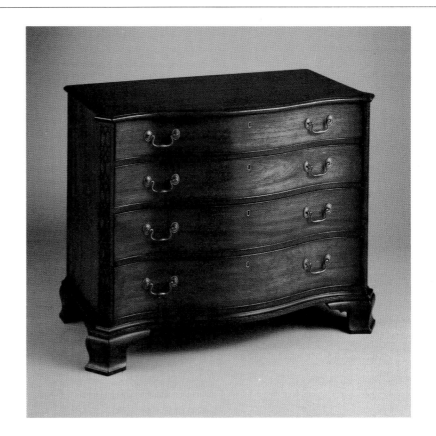

DOUBLE CHEST 39050 (WA 1050)

An important and substantial piece for any room, this handsome chest is marked by its elegance of detail. In mahogany, it has quarter-round turned columns at the corners, paneled ends, and ogee base brackets. The nine drawers are outlined by boxwood inlays and have a highly decorative pattern of simple brass escutcheons and drawer pulls. There are locks on the top three drawers.

Height 34"; length 61½"; depth 22½".

The original of this piece is English, circa 1780, Chippendale (George III).

Detail of the quarter-round tuned column at the corner of the 39050 Chest.

BACHELOR'S CHEST
39068 (CW 68)

An English antique of the mid-eighteenth century, in a hold-over of the Queen Anne style, is the model for this exact reproduction. The drawers are finely graduated, and an intriguing detail is a top slide which turns the piece into a dressing stand. It was called a "bachelor's chest" because of its somewhat smaller size which in no way detracts from its superb design.

Height 29¾"; width 30"; depth 17½".

The original of this piece is in the Ewing House. English, circa 1740, Queen Anne (George II).

BACHELOR'S CHEST
38031 (WA 1031)

This adaptation of an English Chippendale chest reflects the fine, masculine lines of the original. It is beautifully made of grained mahogany, and embellished on both front and side with fine brasses. Its pull-out shelf makes it practical in a dressing room or bedroom, but it can also serve as a small desk in a study.

Height 30½"; length 31¼"; depth 18".

The original of this piece is English, circa 1750, Chippendale (George II).

CHEST 39183 (CW 183)
This serpentine front combined with four graduated drawers create a visual effect of harmony in this chest of drawers. With its smaller size it can easily be used in a corner or in a hallway, accented by a beautiful vase or candlestick.

Height 31¾″; width 37⅞″; depth 21⅞″.

The original of this reproduction is from Massachusetts, circa 1760-1770; Chippendale (George III).

LOWBOY 39019 (CW 19)
Solid elegance marks this lowboy of Chippendale design, based on an antique attributed to a Maryland or Virginia cabinetmaker. The reproduction faithfully duplicates the fluted columns, carved cabriole legs, and fine brass hardware of the original, and is a superb hallway or study piece.

Height 32″; length 38½″; depth 20″.

The original of this piece is American, circa 1760, Chippendale.

Detail of carved leg and foot of 39019 lowboy, with acanthus leaf and claw-and-ball.

HIGHBOY 38062 (WA 1062)

The lower section of this graceful mahogany highboy is distinguished by acorn drops and a deep-stepped ogee arch flanked by shallower ogee arches. The antique was made in New England.

Height 63¼″; width 40⅜″; depth 21¾″.

The original of this piece is in the Powell-Waller House American, circa 1735, Queen Anne.

HIGHBOY 39153 (CW 153)

The original of this highboy, reproduced in mahogany, is believed to have been made in New Jersey. Beautifully proportioned, the highboy stands on four cabriole legs and has a boldly carved and scalloped skirt. It is an elegant and impressive piece for hallway or bedroom.

Height 69¾″; width 42¾″; depth 22⅞″.

The original of this piece is in the upstairs hall of the George Wythe House. American, circa 1760, Chippendale.

COMMODE 38030 (WA 1030)
The original English antique has been copied to form a handsome and practical side table for books and magazines. The deep storage drawer is a useful addition.

Height 31½″; width 23¼″; depth 19″.

The original of this piece is in His Lordship's Bedroom in the Governor's Palace. English, circa 1750, Chippendale (George II).

CANTERBURY 39315 (CW 315)
Introduced in the Federal period as a rack to hold large folios of music, the canterbury remains essentially unchanged in form today. It can still be used for its original purpose, as well as to store and display magazines and large books so that they are readily at hand. This fine mahogany example, copied from an original English canterbury, is useful and convenient beside an easy chair or sofa.

Height 23″; length 20″; width 15⅞″.

The original of this piece is in the Coke-Garrett House, English, circa 1790, Sheraton.

HANGING SHELF 39037 (CW 37)
This mahogany hanging shelf, a typical Thomas Chippendale design, is a reproduction of an old stand of bookshelves. The four shelves and two convenient drawers are united by upright ends of delicate fretwork.

Height 39″; width 36″; depth 7″.

The original of this piece is English, circa 1790, Chippendale (George III).

SHELF

A fine mahogany adaptation of a typical Chippendale piece. Four shelves and a drawer are supported by openwork ends.

38038 (WA 1038). Height 34″; width 30″; depth 7″.

38938 (WA 1038). Height 34″; width 24″; depth 7″.

The original of this piece is English, circa 1760, Chippendale (George III).

BASIN STAND 39005 (CW 5)

This mahogany basin stand reproduces an antique now in Colonial Williamsburg. Doubling nowadays as a charming indoor planter, the 31009 Pewter Bowl fits into the rim of the stand.

Height 32″; diameter 11¾″.

The original of this piece is in the Governor's Palace. English, circa 1740, Queen Anne (George II).

KETTLE STAND 39182 (CW 182)

This kettle stand was designed to hold a cup and saucer in front of a tea urn. Its pedestal has ring turnings at the top and an urn surmounted by a spiral twist below; three cabriole legs support it.

Height 22¾″; top: large 12″ diameter, small 4⅞″ diameter.

The original of this piece is in the Peyton Randolph House. English, circa 1750, Queen Anne (George II).

CANDLESTAND 39049 (CW 49)

This mahogany candlestand, copied from an English provincial antique, matches in detail the original's octagonal top, with gallery, turned stem and tripod base.

Height 38½″; top 10½″ x 10½″.

The original of this piece is English, circa 1740, Queen Anne (George II).

KETTLE STAND 39149 (CW 149)

This mahogany kettle stand with a spun copper top exactly copies an English antique. It is practical as a small moveable table or for a pot of hot-house flowers.

Height 21″; diameter 10″.

The original of this piece is English, circa 1725-1730, Queen Anne (George I).

FIRE SCREEN 39092 (CW 92)

An approved Williamsburg reproduction of an antique English fire screen, the stand, frame and finial are of mahogany.

Height 47½″; panel 17¾″ x 17¾″.

The original of this piece is in the George Wythe House. English, circa 1760, Chippendale (George III).

38038

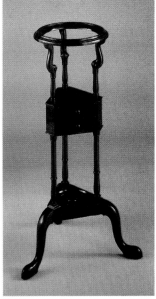

39005

39182

39049

39149

39092

The little middle room of the Governor's Palace.

DOUBLE BED 39058 (CW58)
SINGLE BED 39958 (CW58½)
QUEEN-SIZE BED 39658 (CW58-60)
This bed, with mahogany frame and maple side rails, is reproduced from a late eighteenth-century New England antique. Definitely a lighter construction than those made earlier in the century, the finely turned posts are small and the canopy frame light and arched. The bed can be used without a canopy, thus exposing the delicate finials; it is available either way. Particularly effective in, and complementing, a bedroom with feminine decor. All beds use standard springs and mattresses.

39058 Double Bed.
Height 58½" (with canopy 77⅛"); width 59⅜"; length 81⅜".

39958 Single Bed.
Height 58½" (with canopy 77⅛"); width 44⅜"; length 81⅜".

39658 Queen-size Bed.
Height 58½" (with canopy 77⅛"); width 66⅜"; length 87⅜".

The original of these pieces is American, late 18th century, Hepplewhite.

Detail of the finial on the posts of the 39058 Bed.

Bed frame showing construction.

In this charming bedroom scene the bed hangings are Bluebell Stripe and the bedspread is Wythe House. The bed is 39958. The bedside table is 38059.

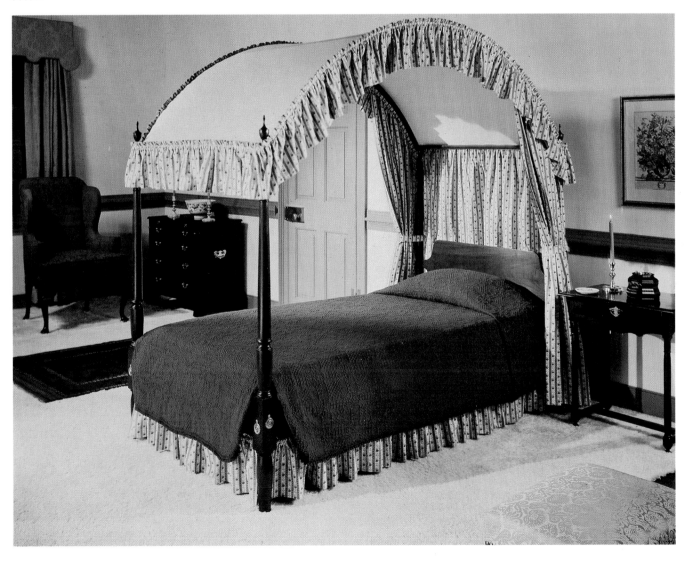

DOUBLE BED 39170 (CW170)
SINGLE BED 39970 (CW170½)
QUEEN-SIZE BED 39670 (CW170-60)
The original from which this bed has
been copied was made of mahogany
by a Newport cabinetmaker. The
elaboration of the front posts above
the rails is unusual.

39170 Double Bed.
Height 95¼"; length 82¾"; width 61⅜".

39970 Single Bed.
Height 95¼"; length 82¾"; width 46⅜".

39670 Queen-Size Bed.
Height 95¼"; length 88¾"; width 68⅜".

Detail of the
spiral carved post
on the 39170 Bed.

Bed frame showing construction.

Bed hangings made from Jones Toile
and finished with Straight Cut Fringe
set off the elegance of the 39970 Bed.

HALF-CANOPY BED
AND FULL-CANOPY BEDS

These beds are adapted from an original made in New England. Beds of this type were produced in all the colonies in the eighteenth century and remained popular over a long period of time. The classic simplicity is ideal for today's living, as the bed fits in perfectly with both formal and informal furnishings of antique or modern design. Available as either a half-canopy or full-canopy bed. All beds use standard springs and mattresses.

38003 (WA 1003) Half-Canopy Bed (Double) and
38063 (WA 1063) Full-Canopy Bed (Double).
Height 79½"; width 56½"; length 79½".

38903 (WA 1003½) Half-Canopy Bed (Single) and
38963 (WA 1063½) Full-Canopy Bed (Single).
Height 79½"; width 41½"; length 79½".

38603 (WA 1003-60) Half-Canopy Bed (Queen Size) and
38663 (WA 1063-60) Full-Canopy Bed (Queen Size).
Height 79½"; width 63½"; length 85½".

Standard size rails for the 38003 and the 38903 beds are 75". They are available, however, in 78" and 81" lengths at no additional cost.

The original of these pieces is in the Raleigh Tavern. American, last half of 18th century, Chippendale.

Bed frame showing construction.

The bed hangings on the 38003 Double Bed and the covering on the 38040 Chair are Williamsburg Iris. The bedspread is William and Mary.

LOW-POST BED

An antique bed made in Newport, Rhode Island, provided the precedent for this adaptation. The curved headboard and deep fluting on the posts are taken from the original. All beds use standard springs and mattresses.

38034 (WA 1034) Double Bed.
Height 40¼"; length 79½"; width 56½".

38934 (WA 1034½) Single Bed.
Height 40¼"; length 79½"; width 41½".

38634 (WA 1034-60) Queen-Size Bed.
Height 40¼"; length 85½"; width 64¼".

Standard side rails for the 38034 and 38934 beds are 75". They are available, however, in 78" and 81" lengths at no additional charge.

The original of these pieces is American, circa 1760-1770, Chippendale.

Bed frame showing construction.

38934

DOUBLE BED 39139 (CW 139)
SINGLE BED 39939 (CW 139½)
QUEEN-SIZE BED 39639 (CW 139-60)
The original of these four-poster
canopy Chippendale bedsteads was
made in New England in the second
half of the eighteenth century. Reproduced in solid mahogany, they have a
flat canopy and tapered headposts
united by an arched headboard. The
footposts are fluted and end in cabriole
legs with bold claw-and-ball feet.
All beds use standard springs and
mattresses.

39139 Double Bed.
Height 87¾″; width 61½″; length 82¼″.

39939 Single Bed.
Height 87¾″; width 46½″; length 82¼″.

39639 Queen-Size Bed.
Height 87¾″; width 68½″; length 88¼″.

The original of these pieces is American,
circa 1760-1775, Chippendale.

Where space allows a gracious bedroom setting, a pair of 39939 twin beds
gives a great warmth and stateliness.
Note the curved design in the canopy,
a striking contrast to the bold Multi-
Stripe fabric (page 150). Other Williamsburg items used to complete this room
are the 38012 Wing Chair in the
foreground, the 39057 Table (between
the beds) with a 35700 Wythe House
Clock, the 39002 Corner Table, and
the 39019 Lowboy on the far wall.

Bed frame showing construction.

Detail of claw-and-ball foot on 39139 bed.

DECORATING WITH *WILLIAMSBURG* FABRICS, WALL COVERINGS, PAINTS AND BEDSPREADS

Visitors to the exhibition buildings of Williamsburg rarely fail to be impressed by the rich and varied use of fabrics and decorative wallpapers. These wall, bed and window coverings maintain a long tradition in the colonial capital. Subdued or exuberant, simple or exotic, they establish the background and set the tone for Williamsburg's historic rooms. The same fabrics and papers can lend a dramatic flair to contemporary rooms, whether they are to be part of a period decor or of a strikingly modern one. They combine an 18th-century decorative genius with the timelessness of beauty and utility.

Wall and window hangings were designed as much to exclude cold and drafts from the room as to beautify it. For the same purpose, the colonial housewife often provided her tall post beds with a substantial array of hangings, in many cases matching the window fabrics. In today's bedrooms a similarly handsome effect is achieved by bedspreads that match or complement the window hangings.

In medieval times tapestries were hung over bare stone walls to give protection against the damp. In later centuries, as construction methods improved, these heavy, thick tapestries evolved into rich silk damasks, especially in the more elegant public and private settings. Handpainted and hand-blocked wallpapers came into use around the time of Williamsburg's origins and extremely fine examples were to be found on the walls of some houses during the eighteenth century.

Williamsburg Fabrics are produced for Craft House by F. Schumacher and Company of New York City, and wallpapers by Katzenbach and Warren, Incorporated, also of New York City. Together, these firms have produced for the Reproductions Program a group of *Williamsburg* color-related fabrics and wallpapers. *Williamsburg* paints are produced by the Martin-Senour Company of Chicago. A wide range of colors, both interior and exterior, represent the variety of hues used throughout Colonial Williamsburg. *Williamsburg* bedspreads are made exclusively by Bates Fabrics, Incorporated, of New York City, and are available in several patterns with a selection of colors.

The originals of these fabric and wallpaper designs have been collected from a variety of sources. Surviving examples of textiles, furniture coverings, bedspreads and damask window hangings are available for copying. Scraps of wallpaper turn up as lining of trunks or bible boxes where, protected from the light, colors have lasted undiminished. Paintings of the period show designs and colors, and drawings, prints and advertisements provide further models. In restoring Williamsburg homes successive layers of wallpaper have been recovered by careful soaking and peeling.

In this modern storage area the Colonial Williamsburg collection of antique textiles is kept free from dust and light. Textiles in the exhibition buildings are constantly changed.

Whereas the Williamsburg furniture tradition is English and American, it is not surprising that the ladies of colonial times looked also to France for their curtains and coverings as well as their frills and furbelows. Readers of this section will soon discover the French inspiration of many of the designs, for this was also the age of Aubusson wall hangings and rugs.

The curatorial staff of Williamsburg has made the identification and use of eighteenth-century fabrics a scientific and artistic life's work. In the restoration of a room, the nature of the background decoration is of overwhelming importance. The same considerations apply to furnishing today's rooms: Color, material and design all enter in, and the function of a room—whether sitting room, bedroom, dining room, even kitchen, den or playroom—helps to determine the choice. Then comes the mood that is desired: formal or informal, simple or elegant. Silk materials enhance the effect of a formal or elaborate decor; cotton may be used to emphasize a simpler or lighter mood. It is well known that larger rooms can use patterns that are bold in color and design, whereas the size of small rooms is enhanced by small and restrained designs.

Williamsburg Fabrics, faithfully reflecting the originals, come in a wealth of materials. These are the finest cottons (calicos toiles, and chintzes); linens; silks and woolens, each with its particular beauty and utility; and woolens woven into elaborate damask, as well as into simpler designs. Today, as in past centuries, weavers combine cotton and flax, cotton and silk, and cotton and wool for special effects.

The heavier materials are particularly suitable for the formal hangings of a sitting or dining room, for upholstery, or for bed coverings. The lighter materials serve especially well in bedrooms, study or playrooms, or to add a seasonal change to other rooms.

In addition to the restored homes and public buildings of Williamsburg, many privately occupied homes demonstrate a most felicitous free mixing of wall and window fabrics of colonial derivation in a variety of settings, together with paintings and accessories that know no period. These homes, some of which are illustrated in color in this catalogue, provide an abundance of decorating ideas that readers may wish to apply to their own homes and decor. Whether it be for a formally appointed dining room or a casual sun room or parlor, an immense range of fabrics and wallpapers and paints are available in colors and designs that have stood the test of time and offer unlimited opportunities of choice.

Documented colors in fabrics, wallpapers, paints, bedspreads, and needlework, which blend and mix together in period and contemporary settings.

Reproduction fabrics from natural fibers—silk, linen, wool and cotton. If a stria occurs in the weave of the antique, it is to be found within the reproduction. Fringes are woven from the same yarns used to weave the fabric.

HOW WINDOWS ARE TREATED

Reference has already been made to the selection of fabrics for a given room, considerations which apply also to the kind of wallpaper used. The practical treatment of windows is a matter for which Williamsburg provides a number of precedents. There are three basic types of window treatment:

In figure A, festoons and jabots (which are side frills) are placed over the floor-length curtains.

In figure B, there are festoons and jabots only, and the jabots hang to the window sill or chair rail.

In figure C, there is a more or less elaborately shaped valance covered by fabric. Curtains generally reach to the floor, although Williamsburg has many examples of valance treatment with curtains reaching to the window sill only.

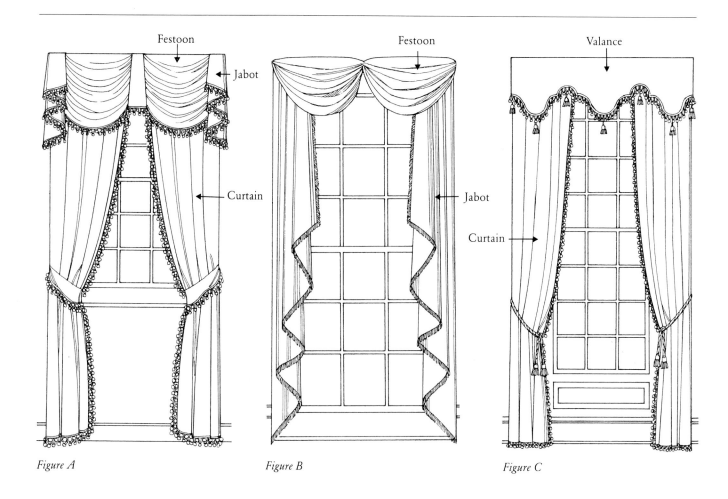

Figure A

Figure B

Figure C

FESTOONS

The number of festoons depends on the width of the window. In Williamsburg, where most windows are only 3½ feet wide, there are two festoons, each of two feet or less (festoons may overlap).

The number of folds in the festoon determines the degree of formality; many folds convey depth and richness while few folds give a sense of lightness.

CURTAINS

Floor-length curtains are always elegant and formal, while hangings to the window sill are informal and at the same time functional, for they keep the curtains away from the floor in an area much used, or difficult to clean.

The most pleasing curtain effects are given by 100% fullness, which means that curtain width should be double that of the window. Most fabrics measure approximately 54 inches; a pair of curtains for a window four feet wide, therefore, requires two widths, one for each curtain.

VALANCES

Valances are subject to many variations. An elaborately shaped and deep valance like the one illustrated in Figure 5, which is in the dining room of the Governor's Palace, represents one extreme and conveys a sense of grandeur with ornateness. Valances used in less formal settings in Williamsburg are illustrated in a series of designs (a to f, page 98). The shape of the valance is also subtly related to the pattern and type of fabric used. A simple valance calls for cottons and small patterns, an intricate design for damasks, a bold design for large fabric patterns.

The proper length of a valance is determined partly by the fabric—longer if it is to accommodate a large and bold pattern, for example. Color plays an essential role because a dark color makes a valance seem smaller, a light color larger, in size. A designer rule of thumb is to allow overall 1½″ to 1¾″ for each foot of window height, modified by the above considerations.

TRIMMINGS

Effects, either formal or informal, can be obtained by trimming in the form of fringe, binding, braid or fabric borders. When used, the trimming should relate to an important color in the fabric. The more ornate hangings are usually trimmed both in valance and festoon as well as the curtains themselves. Ruffles, of course, usually suggest lightness and a touch of informality.

OTHER FEATURES

When maximum light is needed from the window, valances should be kept high up and shallow, and curtains, when drawn back, should not encroach too much on the window panes. Valances should cover everything at the top, including Venetian blind boxes, and should also extend close to the ceiling or molding. Window molding should be left exposed as much as possible.

WILLIAMSBURG WINDOW TREATMENTS

In the illustrations to follow, we see examples of window treatment at Colonial Williamsburg. These offer to the homemaker and decorator multiple suggestions of desirable effects to be used in one's own residence.

Figures 1 to 12 illustrate the many combinations used in Williamsburg.

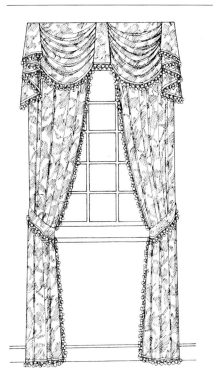

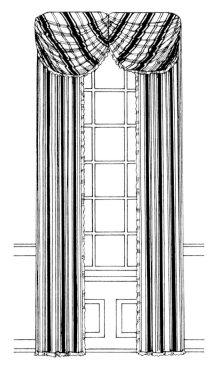

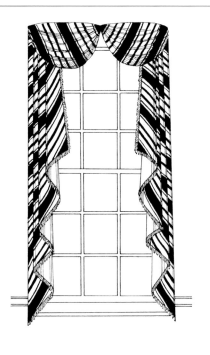

Figure 1
FORMAL
Multi-folded festoons and jabots
over floor-length curtains. All are trimmed
with fringes.

Figure 2
FESTOON
Fringe on multi-folded festoon and curtain.
Formal treatment.

Figure 3
FESTOON AND JABOT
Multi-pleated festoon with jabots to window
sill. Edges fringed in color of fabric.

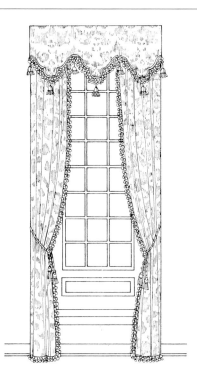

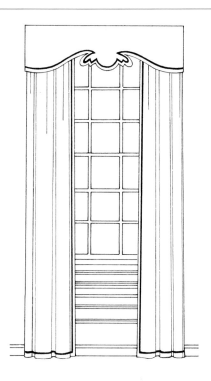

Figure 4
SWAG AND JABOT
Jabots extend to chair rail and so comple-
ment an architectural feature of the room.

Figure 5
ELABORATE VALANCE WITH TRIM
Elaborate valance with three deep scallops.
Large patterned fabric determines height of
valance. Heavy trimmings for a sumptuous
effect.

Figure 6
VALANCE WITH STRAIGHT
CURTAINS AND TAILORED TRIM
Shaped valance with plain fabric is formal
but simple. Binding at edge of valance and
front and bottom of curtains.

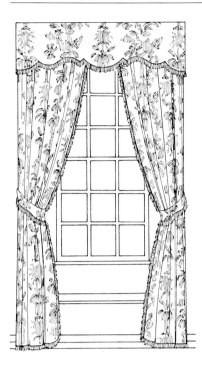

Figure 7
DAMASK FABRIC WITH FRINGE TRIM
Shaped valance with designed fabric for a formal setting.

Figure 8
SEMI-FORMAL CURTAINS WITH SHAPED VALANCE
Shaped valance with designed fabric. Binding at edge of valance and curtains reflect dominant color of pattern.

Figure 9
INFORMAL STRAIGHT CURTAINS WITH SIMPLE VALANCE
Informal draperies in cotton fabric, using plain trim on valance.

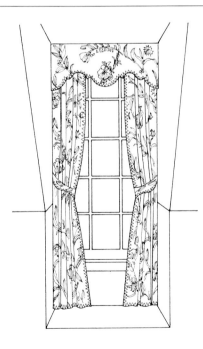

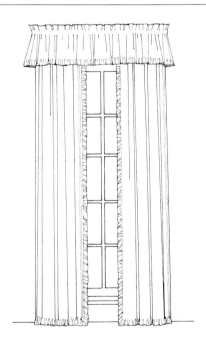

Figure 10
SHAPED VALANCE AND STRAIGHT CURTAIN WITH FABRIC TRIM
Bold free cotton fabric makes valance appear less formal in spite of its details.

Figure 11
DORMER WINDOW TREATMENT WITH SHAPED VALANCE
Short draperies may be enhanced by bold valance and fabric for either formal or informal usage.

Figure 12
STRAIGHT CURTAIN WITH VALANCE
Simple valance with pleated material and bold trimming.

VALANCE DESIGNS USED IN COLONIAL WILLIAMSBURG

a. A soft-shaped valance of regular and inverted scallops. This relatively informal design calls for a small-patterned or figured fabric.

b. A more formal valance than a, and more suitable for a fabric with a large design.

c. "Dog ear" valance, an English design. It is suited to fabrics with an over-all or flowing pattern.

d. A more formal "dog ear" valance with an oriental motif in its pagoda shape. The design is most appropriate for a more formal fabric.

  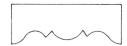 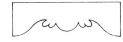

e. A Chippendale-type design. This valance is suitable with a large patterned formal fabric.

f. A design in the European style. Large-patterned fabrics are suitable here.

g. A transitional shape. This valance is adaptable to most fabrics, whether the design is an over-all or a definite pattern.

h. A versatile design taken from an antique in the Williamsburg collection. It is suitable for a plain or small-patterned fabric.

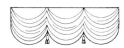 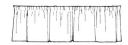

i. Soft festoons calling for a damask or similar formal fabric. The shape is influenced by French designs of the eighteenth century.

j. A single shirred valance. This simple, easy-to-make design is appropriate for an informal fabric.

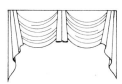 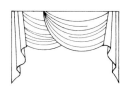 

k. A treatment similar to Jefferson's sketches of hangings at Monticello. This festoon and jabot design is formal and best suited to damasks.

l. A very formal, heavily draped treatment with a French feeling. It is late-eighteenth-century and is most often used with damasks.

m. A less formal treatment using festoons alone. This valance design can be adapted to most fabrics.

BED HANGINGS

The ideal treatment for beds can be seen in the Craft House and in the bedrooms of the Wythe House where the valances at the top of canopy beds have the same design as the window valance. Generally window fabrics are repeated in those of the bed. On field beds (those with a strongly arched canopy) gathered or shirred valances give a light, informal effect and this can be repeated at the windows.

The dressing of a bed, tall post or not, needs careful attention to the bedspread. It may complement or relate to the bed or window hangings. Solid color bedspreads may be used with printed fabrics in any decor.

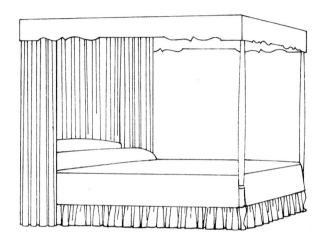

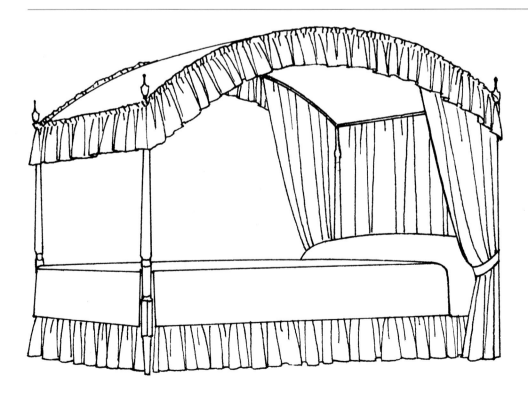

CORRECT METHOD FOR MEASURING THE MOST USUAL KINDS OF WINDOWS

A. Extreme Width
B. Inside Width
C. Top of Trim to Ceiling

D. Extreme Height
E. Inside Height
F. Sill to Floor
G. Return

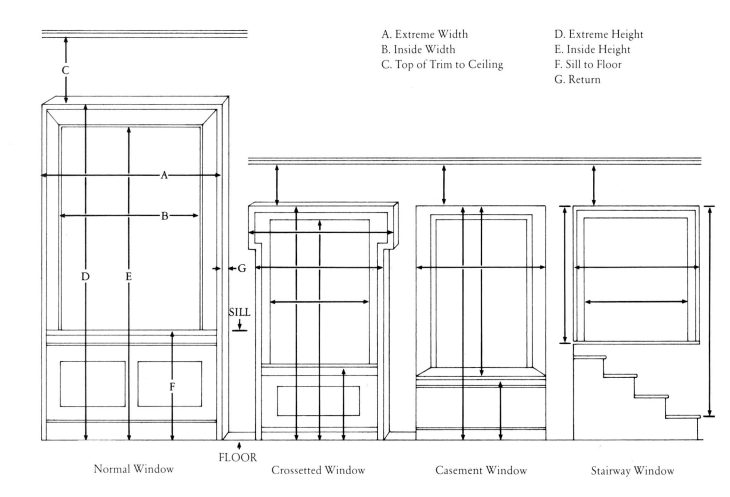

Normal Window   Crossetted Window   Casement Window   Stairway Window

CRAFT HOUSE DECORATING ADVISORY SERVICE

For many years, Craft House has offered decorating advice informally on request. Demand for such assistance has grown to the point where we have established a new Craft House Decorating Advisory Service to better assist individuals, corporations or professional decorators.

The Craft House Decorating Advisory Service staff welcomes all inquiries and will advise on the use of Williamsburg Reproductions. For assistance, at no charge, call 804-229-1000 or write Box CH, Williamsburg, Virginia 23187.

Williamsburg fabrics, wall coverings and paints offer the home, corporate or professional decorator a wide range of colors, patterns and textures that can be combined to create moods and color schemes of almost unlimited number.

To assist you in combining the many choices, the Craft House Decorating Advisory Service has suggested, in the chart that follows, a number of combinations of fabric designs and colorations with wall covering patterns and colorations together with leather and paint colors. Using this guide, one can see the wide variety of choices available. Color samples are available on request.

PRINTED & WOVEN FABRICS	LEATHER	WALLPAPER	PAINT	INTERIOR PAINT*
String of Pearls, Green Chinese Peony Damask, Blue Williamsburg Dobby Weave, Jade	Shrub		Hyde Park Blue Bassett Hall Green	Palace Chambers Yellow
String of Pearls, Brown Ludwell Adaptation Damask, Opaline Blue Williamsburg Dobby Weave, Walnut	Walnut		Duke of Gloucester Beige Coach House Green	Palace Chambers Green
Williamsburg Floral Stripe, Blue Fleurette Adaptation, Document Blue Williamsburg Wool, Cream	Antique Blue Smoke	Floral Stripe, Blue	Wetherburn's Pale Blue	Palace Parlour Cream
Apples, Gold Williamsburg Dobby Weave, Fern	Thrush Camel	Apples, Gold & Olive	Coach House Green	Wetherburn's Tavern Bisque
Williamsburg Potpourri, Buff Williamsburg Wool, Rust Chinese Peony Damask, Blue	Dusk Rust	Potpourri, Blue & Rose on Beige	Palace Study Blue	Blue Bell Tavern Buff

PRINTED & WOVEN FABRICS	LEATHER	WALLPAPER	PAINT	INTERIOR PAINT*
Williamsburg Bluebell Stripe, Blue & Putty Williamsburg Dobby Weave, Taupe Tulip, Marine Blue	Dusk Camel	Williamsburg Bluebell Stripe, Beige	Daphne Room Beige	 Brown House Beige
Williamsburg Flowering Tree, Ruby Wythe House Stripe, Old Red Williamsburg Dobby Weave, Spruce	Mulberry Turquoise		Brown House Beige	 Red Lion Inn Gray
Jones Toile, Dark Pewter Shir O Shakkar, Periwinkle Williamsburg Wool, Cream	Smoke		Wetherburn's Pale Blue Apollo Room Blue	 Chiswell Gray
Chinese Bells, Earth Coral Ludwell Adaptation Damask, Celedon Williamsburg Wool, Brick	Smoke	Mary Lloyd, Gold	Bassett Hall Green	 Red Lion Inn Green
Chinese Bells, Earth Coral Williamsburg Wool, Sage Scotch Cloth Adaptation, Green/Salmon	Glazed Brick Tangerine	Brighton, Coral	Wythe House Gold	 Prentis Store Gray Green
Wood Floral, Blue & Red Williamsburg Dobby Weave, Red Edinburgh Check, Tobacco	Walnut		Wetherburn's Tavern Bisque Palmer House Brown	 Purdie House Gray
Apples, Turquoise Williamsburg Wool, Blue	Periwinkle	Apples, Olive Blue & Green	Scrivener Kitchen Gold	 Palace Supper Room Pale Yellow
Parsley, Umber Williamsburg Wool, Gold Williamsburg Wool, Cream	Antique Gold Pirate Gold	Williamsburg Liner Stripe, Mustard	Parlour Cream	 Scrivener Kitchen Gold
Williamsburg Liner Stripe, Deep Yellow Williamsburg Wool, Gold Williamsburg Wool, Cream	Antique Gold Pirate Gold	Williamsburg Liner Stripe, Mustard	Parlour Cream	 Powell-Waller Gold

PRINTED & WOVEN FABRICS	LEATHER	WALLPAPER	PAINT	INTERIOR PAINT*
Raleigh Tavern Resist, Sage Williamsburg Wool, Cream Tavern Check, Sage	Smoke Camel	Tavern Resist, Gold	Palace Ballroom Ceiling White	Daphne Room Beige
Parsley, Spruce Williamsburg Wool, Spruce Williamsburg Wool, Rust	Glazed Black Camel	Country Linen, Brown	Nicolson House Green	Blair House Buff
Apples, Copper Williamsburg Dobby Weave, Copper	Camel Terracotta	Apples, Tangerine & Olive	Brick House Light Peach	James Geddy Tan
Wythe House Floral, Red & Blue Williamsburg Wool, Blue Williamsburg Dobby Weave, Taupe	Thrush	Wythe House Floral, Red & Blue	Supper Room Baseboard	Chownings Tavern Rose Tan
Pintado Stripe, Red-Blue Williamsburg Wool, Turquoise Herringbone Strie, Rust	Smoke Thrush	Pintado Stripe, Red & Blue	Powell-Waller Red	Raleigh Tavern Tan
Tracery Floral, Spruce w/Tan Williamsburg Dobby Weave, Biscuit Williamsburg Wool, Rust	Glazed Black Camel		Raleigh Tavern Tan Palmer House Brown	Brick House Light Peach
Morning Glory, Red Bruton Adaptation Damask, Crimson Williamsburg Dobby Weave, Marine Blue		Morning Glories, Red	Palace Dining Room Pearl Blue	Williamsburg Simulated Whitewash
Botanical Chintz, Blue & Red Herringbone Strie, Aqua Herringbone Strie, Rust	Blackberry		Wetherburn's Pale Blue Powell-Waller Red	Palace Ballroom Ceiling White
Williamsburg Potpourri, Greenwood Wren Williamsburg Wool, Sage Williamsburg Wool, Gold	Antique Gold	Potpourri, Ochre & Rose on Olive	Supper Room Baseboard Brown	Russell House Green

PRINTED & WOVEN FABRICS	LEATHER	WALLPAPER	PAINT	INTERIOR PAINT*
Pondicherry, Coral Bruton Adaptation Damask, Salmon Williamsburg Wool, Gold		Aviary, Green	Parlour Cream	Bassett Hall Green
Flower Leaf Stripe, Willow Williamsburg Dobby Weave, Jade			Blair House Buff Powell-Waller Red	Coach House Green
Williamsburg Flowering Tree, Ruby Chinese Peony Damask, Rose Liverpool Birds, Sage Green	Oyster Myrtle	Stencil Square, Dark Celadon	Williamsburg Simulated Whitewash	Nicolson House Green
Williamsburg Stripe, Red & Green Tulip, Hunter Green		Tulip, Green	Wythe House Gold	Market Square Green
Flowered Print, Natural Williamsburg Wool, Spruce Williamsburg Wool, Burgundy	Patina Red Myrtle	Flowered Print, Rose & Celedon	Palace Chambers Yellow	Raleigh Tavern Green
Bluebell Stripe, Sulphur Williamsburg Dobby Weave, Sky Blue Williamsburg Wool, Cream	Sky Blue Gold	Bluebell Stripe, Gold	Wythe House Gold	Apothecary Shop Blue
Banyan Print, Green & Gold Liverpool Birds, Celadon Williamsburg Wool, Gold		Stencil Square, Gold on Mustard	Russell House Green	Wythe House Gold
Botanical Chintz, Natural Williamsburg Dobby Weave, Peach Williamsburg Dobby Weave, Pecan	Honey	Hyde Park, Charcoal	Brick House Light Peach	Pelham Gray
Pineapple and Poppy, Red & Beige Wythe House Stripe, Old Red Williamsburg Dobby Weave, Taupe	Magenta Ebony		Brown House Beige Campbell's Tavern Charcoal	Peyton Randolph Gray

PRINTED & WOVEN FABRICS	LEATHER	WALLPAPER	PAINT	INTERIOR PAINT*
Calico Bird, Rose Dust Williamsburg Dobby Weave, Brick Red Williamsburg Wool, Sage	Gold Dust	Calico Bird, Rose Dust	Powell-Waller Red	Raleigh Tavern Peach
Calico Bird, Red, White & Blue Liverpool Birds, Turkey Red Williamsburg Wool, Blue	Antique Blue Lacquer	Calico Bird, Red, White & Blue	Raleigh Tavern Chinese Red	King's Arms Rose Pink
Williamsburg Floral Trails, Blue Chinese Peony Damask, Blue Williamsburg Wool, Williamsburg Blue	Copenhagen Smoke	Madison, Blue on Oyster	Brush-Everard Blue	Wetherburn's Pale Blue
Williamsburg Potpourri, Moonstone Blue Fleurette Adaptation, Blue Williamsburg Wool, Rust	Dusk Smoke	Potpourri, Rose & Blue on Aqua	Supper Room Baseboard Brown	Palace Dining Room Pearl Blue
Williamsburg Iris, Blue Williamsburg Stripe, Coral & Blue Chinese Peony Damask, Blue	Copenhagen	Williamsburg Iris, Blue	Palace Parlour Cream	Palace Study Blue
Williamsburg Potpourri, Old Rose Herringbone Stripe, Rust & Blue Williamsburg Wool, Blue	Lacquer Copenhagen	Potpourri, Red & Blue on Brick	Palace Parlour Cream	Apollo Room Blue
Raleigh Tavern Resist, Brick Red Apples, Brick Williamsburg Wool, Cream	Terracotta Pirate Gold	Tavern Resist, Red	Scrivener Kitchen Gold	Powell-Waller Red
Bruton Resist, Midnight Blue Edinburgh Check, Blue & Red Williamsburg Wool, Navy	Lacquer	Bruton Resist, Midnight	Williamsburg Simulated Whitewash	Raleigh Tavern Chinese Red
Williamsburg Grapes, Amber & Green Williamsburg Check, Ochre Williamsburg Dobby Weave, Olive Green	Spanish Gold Imperial Gold	Coach House, Green	Wythe House Gold	Palmer House Brown

PRINTED & WOVEN FABRICS	LEATHER	WALLPAPER	PAINT	INTERIOR PAINT*
Pondicherry, Lavender & Pink Bruton Adaptation Damask, Crimson Williamsburg Wool, Crimson	Ruby	Pondicherry, Red & Blue	Parlour Cream	Brush-Everard Blue
Flower Leaf Stripe, Saddle Tan Williamsburg Wool, Rust Williamsburg Dobby Weave, Biscuit	Saddle		Powell-Waller Red James Geddy Tan	James Southall Blue
Banyan Print, Red & Blue Bruton Adaptation Damask, Crimson Williamsburg Wool, Cream			Williamsburg Simulated Whitewash Wetherburn's Pale blue	Brafferton Blue
Lozenge Floral, Cranberry & Brown Williamsburg Dobby Weave, Red Williamsburg Dobby Weave, Taupe	Ebony	Bird and Acorn, Red	Brown House Beige	James Geddy Gray
Tavern Check, Gold Williamsburg Wool, Cream	Pirate Gold Tobacco	Williamsburg Tavern Check, Gold	Powell-Waller Gold	Campbell's Tavern Charcoal Brown
Tracery Floral, Brass Williamsburg Wool, Cocoa Williamsburg Dobby Weave, Taupe	Apple Tobacco		Raleigh Tavern Tan Chowning's Tavern Rose Tan	Palace Summer Room Brown

*The colors shown here may be affected by age, light and printing methods and may vary somewhat from actual paint colors. Variations in surface texture, lighting and application may also influence the color effect of the painted surface.

ORDERING FABRICS, WALL COVERINGS, PAINTS AND BEDSPREADS
Color samples of *Williamsburg* Fabrics are available upon request; small cotton samples fifty cents per pattern, with full color range when specified; silk damask samples one dollar deposit per sample. Large samples of fabrics are also available on a loan basis; a deposit equivalent to the price per yard is requested. Deposits are refunded when samples are returned within the thirty-day loan period.

A large Wallpaper catalogue of *Williamsburg* wall coverings will be sent on a loan for a deposit of ten dollars plus a shipping charge of three dollars. The deposit will be refunded when the catalogue is returned within thirty days. For those wishing to keep the catalogue for a longer period of time, there is an additional charge of forty dollars. Please note that although wallpaper is priced by the single roll, it is packed in double or triple rolls.

Paint charts of the complete line of *Williamsburg* exterior and interior colors are available at no charge. Please direct your request to Craft House, Dept. 1, Box CH, Williamsburg, Virginia 23187. Many of the interior paints are sold not only in full, but also, let-down strengths. These variations are illustrated on the chart.

A limited supply of *Williamsburg* bedspread-sample brochures is also available on a loan basis. A deposit of one dollar per sample is requested and is refunded when the sample is returned within the thirty-day loan period.

Stencil Square wallpaper lends light and drama to this handsome entrance hall. The arm chair is 39942.

Williamsburg®

WALLPAPERS BY KATZENBACH AND WARREN

The skilled craftsmen of Katzenbach and Warren have copied many of Colonial Williamsburg's rare documents to produce their outstanding selection of exquisite Williamsburg Wallpaper Reproductions. Many of these designs derive from eighteenth-century wallpaper fragments found under layers of modern paint and paper on the walls of colonial buildings. Some were discovered lining old trunks and dispatch boxes. Still other patterns are based on antique textiles from the Williamsburg collection, and keyed to the modern fabric reproductions. Each design has been accurately reproduced in the colors of the original, as well as in a wide range of other colors.

In addition to the authentic reproductions, commemorative wallpapers which depict Williamsburg art, architecture, and life are available in a variety of color combinations.

Most Williamsburg wallpapers are manufactured with a protective stain-resistant coating for carefree use in bathroom, kitchen or nursery, and are pretrimmed for ease in hanging. A large wallpaper catalogue will be sent on loan for a deposit plus mailing charges. Deposit will be refunded if the catalogue is returned within 30 days. For those who wish to keep the catalogue for a longer period, there is an additional charge.

Please note that although wallpaper is priced by the single roll, it is packed only in double rolls or triple rolls.

For additional information please write Craft House.

SUPPER ROOM COMMEMORATIVE

This paper is a superb adaptation by Katzenbach and Warren of a magnificent Chinese wallpaper. The hand-painted antique paper has been reduced in scale and a few panels eliminated in order to suit the homes of today. All the grace and color of the original are captured in this commemorative design, and most of the exquisite details of the old paper have been carefully copied. For instance, all of the birds are in pairs, except for the owl who has no mate. Dragonflies, bees, a spider's delicate web, a caterpillar, and even a few flies and mosquitoes have been artfully reproduced in this fine paper.

The two panels that make up the paper, "The Doves" and "The Ducks" (both shown below), are available printed on a wide range of ground colors.

The Ducks

The Doves

108

DORSET
The original of this reproduction wall-paper is used as lining in an early nineteenth century box presently in the collections of Colonial Williamsburg. Sprigs and oval decoration offer an eye soothing pattern which would enhance any room in your home. Sold in double rolls.

Single roll 6 yds. x 24″; repeat 9¼″.

INDIAN FLOWERS
The motif of this wallpaper draws its inspiration from a mid-eighteenth-century Indian textile. Probably part of the Dutch trade, the original fabric is block printed and mordant painted with a striking and unusual motif. The related fabric is shown on page 147. Sold in double rolls.

Single roll 7 yds. x 20″; repeat 12½″.

HYDE PARK
The original is a block print paper of about 1830. It was used to cover a hat box. In the early nineteenth-century band boxes were used as luggage by most levels of society. Colonial Williamsburg has reproduced this charming outer paper for use as an unusual wallpaper. Sold in double rolls.

Single roll 7 yds. x 20″; repeat 19″.

JARDIN CHINOIS

A fanciful chinoiserie pattern of gazebos and floral designs will add a lighthearted touch to your room. Adapted from the cotton fabric of the same design (see page 146), this wallpaper shows the versatility of eighteenth-century patterns. Sold in double rolls.

Single roll 7 yds. x 20″. repeat 12½″.

PLYMOUTH

The linear pattern of this wallpaper was reproduced from a wallpaper used to decoratively frame a painting of a ship. The original is a block print dating from about 1820. Sold in double rolls.

Single roll 7 yds. x 20″; repeat 4¾″.

CALICO BIRD

This wallpaper's pattern was adapted from a late eighteenth or early nineteenth-century French textile. The reproduction fabric can be seen on page 136. Its whimsical charm and delightful colorways would create a beautiful setting for anyone young at heart. Sold in double rolls.

Single roll 6 yds. x 24″; repeat 14¼″.

WILLIAMSBURG IRIS

A crisp, flowing print with a large repeat decorates this wallpaper related to a cotton fabric of the same design. See page 151. This design also inspired a dinnerware pattern by Wedgwood. Illustrated on page 220. Sold in triple rolls.

Single roll 5 yds. x 26″. repeat 36″.

PEYTON RANDOLPH

In the second story Parlor of the Peyton Randolph House is an English mid-eighteenth century flocked wallpaper. This paper has been adapted from the original to better suit today's needs. The integrity of the design has been beautifully preserved and will prove a focal point in your decorating scheme. Sold in triple rolls.

Single roll 5 yds. x 27″. repeat 36″.

BRIGHTON

Block-printed about 1785, the original wallpaper is English and handcolored. The delightful scene of two Chinese boys shows the English fascination with all things oriental during that time period. This lighthearted adaptation with its exotic motifs would enliven even a formal decor. Sold in triple rolls.

Single roll 5 yds. x 27″; repeat 36″.

WINDHAM

With a tradition of coming from the Zaddock Pratt homestead, the classical elements of this circa 1800 paper are reminiscent of any earlier era. Often designed for use in a specific room, this reproduction wallpaper is suitable for a hall or stairway. Sold in double rolls.

Single roll 8 yds. x 18½"; repeat 21¼".

EDINBURGH CHECK

Checked wallpaper gives a country feeling to your kitchen or bath. The original linen fabric from which the pattern was taken dates from the second half of the eighteenth century. When hung with its complimentary fabric (see page 152.) a warm and cozy room will be created. Sold in triple rolls.

Single roll 5 yds. x 27"; repeat 2".

COUNTRY LINEN

This linen-textured wallpaper is available in a number of rich colors to set off your furnishings and accessories. The document fabric is a linen grain bag, probably American in origin. Sold in double rolls.

Single roll 6¼ yds x 22½".

BIRD AND ACORN

The document colors of black on deep curry enhance the cleancut lines of this Bird and Acorn wallpaper, copied from a book paper printed about 1800. The design is available in other striking color combinations for use in today's homes. Sold in double rolls.

Single roll 7 yds x 20"; repeat 15¾".

AVIARY

A delight for bird lovers, this charming wallpaper depicts about a dozen birds, with notes on their care and habits. It was adapted from a linen handkerchief entitled "The Aviary or the Bird Fancyers Recreation." Originally copperplate-printed about 1770, the fine detail provides lasting interest in rooms that are frequently used. Sold in triple rolls.

The reproduction handkerchief may be seen on page 268.

Single roll 5 yds x 28"; repeat 28"

BLUEBELL STRIPE

An eighteenth-century English quilt inspired this dainty pattern of stripes and trailing vines of bluebells. In addition to the wallpaper, Bluebell Stripe has been reproduced in a fabric, shown on page 152. Pleasant for young girls' rooms. Sold in double rolls.

Single roll 7 yds x 20½".

HOMESPUN STRIPE

Soft warm colors and homespun texture distinguish this unusual striped wallpaper. Its design was inspired by an eighteenth-century woolen blanket which was woven in America and is now part of the Williamsburg collection. Sold in double rolls.

Single roll 6¼ yds x 22½"

FLOWERED PRINT

This cheerful design was adapted from a French block-printed textile made about 1780. It is strewn with colorful flowers, vines, leaves and berries. For the fabric, see page 142. Sold in double rolls.

Single roll 8 yds x 18"; repeat 10½"

PALACE GARDEN DAMASK

This lavish pattern of flowers and leaves is inspired by a fabric document of the second quarter of the eighteenth century. Benjamin Bucktrout, Williamsburg cabinetmaker, advertised paper hangings, including damask, for sale in the Virginia Gazette of May 9, 1771. Sold in triple rolls.

Single roll 5 yds x 25¾"; repeat 22"

PINTADO STRIPE

A light and airy wallpaper pattern taken from an antique fabric dating from about 1775, probably of French origin. (The name, from Portuguese 'pinta' for "spotted," was used in the seventeenth century to designate painted cottons—chintz—from India). Related fabric is on page 150. Sold in double rolls.

Single roll 8 yds x 18″; repeat 10½″

WILLIAMSBURG APPLES

Slender stripes and stylized apples adapted from an eighteenth-century quilt lining make up this delightful wallpaper. The fabric reproduction is on page 143. Sold in double rolls.

Single roll 7 yds x 20½″; repeat ¼″

LITTLE CROWNS

Rows of miniature crowns march across this commemorative paper, inspired by the crown of William III, in whose honor the city of Williamsburg was named. Sold in double rolls.

Single roll 7 yds x 20″

COLONIAL MOLDINGS

These unusual papers were inspired by architectural features frequently found in the homes and buildings of eighteenth-century Virginia, which you might want to simulate today. Cornice and Chair Rail (sold by the single roll containing 10 yards of cornice, 10 yards of chair rail and 10 pairs of profile ends). Wainscot (sold by the single roll containing 5 yards).

WILLIAMSBURG COMMEMORATIVE SCENIC

This handsome hand-printed paper consists of seven strips, each 27 inches wide trimmed, for a total width of 15 feet 9 inches. As illustrated below, the strips show Bruton Parish Church, the Governor's Palace, the Magazine and the Guardhouse, the Courthouse of 1770, the Raleigh Tavern, and the Capitol. Not shown is the Garden, a filler strip which may be used anywhere to allow buildings or groups of buildings to be centered. Height of the patterns varied from 12½ inches in the Garden to 22¼ inches the Governor's Palace. It is quite handsome as a decorative border on a painted wall, or also when used to paper an entire wall or room. Also available in double size. Write for further information.

Left to right: Bruton Parish Church, The Governor's Palace, The Magazine and Guardhouse

MORNING GLORY

Undulating morning glory vines and C scrolls are interwined with three narrow ribbon stripes developing an exotic scheme. Copied from a French copperplate chintz dating circa 1775, this wallpaper will be the highlight in any room. The reproduction fabric can be seen on page 133. Sold in double rolls.

Single roll 8 yds. x 18″. repeat 36″.

Left to right: The Courthouse of 1770, The Raleigh Tavern, The Capitol

CHARLES II

The original paper which inspired this charming reproduction probably dates from about 1660. Figures representing the four seasons surround a circle containing a lion, unicorn, and the crowns of England, Scotland, and Ireland. It is one of the oldest English lining papers extant. Sold in double rolls.

Single roll 7 yds. x 20¼"; repeat 14¼"

PONDICHERRY

Copied from an East Indian painted cotton fabric, the trailing vines and flowers create a delicate and airy design. The color related fabric is on page 146. Sold in double rolls.

Single roll 6 yds. x 25"; repeat 18".

STENCIL FLOWERS

Block print flowers and vines in alternating columns form the pattern in this striking wallpaper copied from an eighteenth-century resist-dyed textile. The color related fabric is on page 148. Sold in double rolls.

Single roll 6 yds. x 25; repeat 12½".

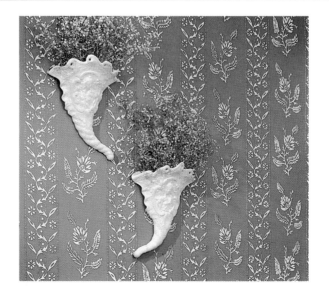

WILLIAMSBURG TAVERNS

Four famous taverns of Colonial Wiliamsburg are illustrated on this commemorative wallpaper. Included are Christiana Campbell's, Josiah Chowning's, the King's Arms, and the Raleigh Tavern. Sold in triple rolls.

Single roll 5 yds. x 27"; repeat 19".

DIAMOND FLORAL

Continental European influence may be seen in this lively pattern taken from a French textile. The reproduction fabric may be seen on page 144. Sold in double rolls.

Single roll 7 yds. x 19½"; repeat 8".

FOX GRAPE

The original wallpaper with its lattice-work design was found on the walls of a closet in the Nicolson Shop in Williamsburg. It is believed to be the same design ordered by Thomas Jefferson from Paris in 1790 for use in his Philadelphia home. There is evidence that the same paper was also used at Monticello. Sold in double rolls.

Single roll 18 yds. x 18"; repeat 18¾".

YARMOUTH

Flowers, dots and scalloped stripes provide the unusual design of this reproduction wallpaper copied from the antique of about 1800. Sold in double rolls.

Single roll 8 yds. x 18¼"; repeat 6¼".

MADISON

The wallpaper lining, of probable French origin, of an early nineteenth-century American trunk was copied to provide this paper decorated with graceful flowering tendrils, flowers and fragile shoots. Sold in double rolls.

Single roll 6½ yds. x 21½"; repeat 21".

FLORAL SQUARES

A charming arrangement of delicately-drawn floral squares, this pattern is copied from a block-printed paper found as a lining in a seventeenth-century Bible box. The original was made in England about 1680. Sold in triple rolls.

Single roll 5 yds x 28"; repeat 10½".

POTPOURRI

Adapted from the cotton fabric of the same design (see page 151). This entrancing pattern is a rich medley of birds, flowers and fruits. A dinnerware pattern by Wedgwood has also been inspired by Potpourri. Sold in double rolls.

Single roll 6¼ yds. x 21″; repeat 21″.

TULIP

This charming floral pattern has been copied from a European textile of the late seventeenth century. Its neat blocks of stylized flowers and leaves are reproduced in a related fabric, shown on page 150. Sold in double rolls.

Single roll 7 yds x 20″; repeat 4″.

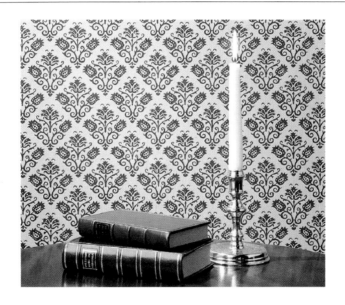

RALEIGH TAVERN

Bouquets of stylized flowers alternate with undulating ribbon stripes entwined with blossoms in this striking paper. It was adapted from an antique French fabric, and is availale in a variety of colors. The related fabric, Raleigh Tavern Resist, is shown on page 149. Sold in double rolls.

Single roll 6 yds x 24″; repeat 22″.

FLORAL STRIPE

An eighteenth-century French cotton fabric inspired this rich design, in which bouquets of flowers on undulating ribbons alternate with wide bands of stylized flowers. The related fabric is described on page 141. Sold in double rolls.

Single roll 7 yds x 20½"; repeat 12½"

LAFAYETTE FLORAL

Another colonial town, Kennebunkport, Maine, is the source of the English eighteenth-century wallpaper fragment from which this charming floral design was copied. This antique paper now rests in the Williamsburg Collection. Sold in double rolls.

Single roll 7 yds x 20½"; repeat 22"

MULTI-STRIPE

Crisp and fresh-looking, this striped paper was copied from an old fabric in the Williamsburg collection. A popular design in the eighteenth century, it is gaining popularity again in both paper and fabric (see page 150). Sold in double rolls.

Single roll 8 yds x 19"

MARY LLOYD

This airy and elegant floral pattern was copied from the lining paper of an antique leather box. A label in the box identifies Mary Lloyd as a trunkmaker "at the corner of Pudding-Row, Opposite Winetavern Street, Dublin." The delicacy of this wallpaper opens up long, narrow rooms and hallways. Sold in double rolls.

Single roll 7 yds x 20"; repeat 22"

WYTHE HOUSE FLORAL

The borders of the Wythe House Floral cotton fabric (see page 137) inspired this graceful wallpaper pattern. In the wallpaper, the borders combine for a striped effect; in the fabric they simply frame a large flowering vine. Sold in double rolls.

Single roll 7 yds x 20"; repeat 11"

WILLIAMSBURG CHECK

An antique linen tabby-weave fabric in the Williamsburg collection inspired this crisp-looking checked wallpaper, available in a wide variety of fresh, attractive colors. The fabric reproduction is described on page 153. Sold in double rolls.

Single roll 7 yds x 20″

WILLIAMSBURG BRUTON RESIST

Reproduced from an 18th-century resist-dyed fabric, this unusual wallpaper design is available in many stunning colors. Stylized chrysanthemums, lilacs, and fern-like leaves make up the pattern. The related linen fabric is on page 142. Sold in double rolls.

Single roll 7 yds x 20½″; repeat 12½″

WILLIAMSBURG LINER STRIPE

This delicate pattern of lacy stripes is copied from the border tape used on antique bed hangings in the James Geddy House. The same design is used in a related fabric of 100% cotton, illustrated on page 140. Sold in double rolls.

Single roll 6 yds x 24″

WILLIAMSBURG STRIPE

An eighteenth-century Italian antique textile inspired both this handsome wallpaper design and its related fabric, seen on page 144, in a rich silk and cotton combination. Stripes of varying widths are woven into dramatic design, available in a wide range of colors. This striking wallpaper is attractive in a young man's bedroom, a den, or family room. Sold in double rolls.

Single roll 6 yds x 24¼″

125

WILLIAMSBURG TAVERN CHECK

The crisp look of a starched tablecloth is carried over into this boldly checked wallpaper copied from an early American textile. It is available in a wide range of gay colors, suitable for kitchen, dining room or family room. A related fabric in linen and cotton is shown in page 141. Sold in double rolls.

Single roll 7 yds x 19½"; repeat 3"

WINTERBERRY

Found in a late eighteenth-century home in Melrose, Massachusetts, this dotted stripe with vertical bands of a conventional leaf motif is a delightfully delicate pattern. Crisp and cheerful, this wallpaper has the treasured quality of timelessness. Sold in double rolls.

Single roll 6 yds x 22"; repeat 5¼"

126

STENCIL SQUARE

In hallway, kitchen, dining room or family room, this handsome geometric pattern suits today's way of life. Copied from an antique fragment in the Williamsburg collection, this classic paper is available in the document colors of blue on taupe and other rich color combinations. Sold in double rolls.

Single roll 8 yds x 19''; repeat 19''

MANDARIN AND PINE TREE

East meets West in this dramatic reproduction wallpaper, which gracefully combines English flowers with Oriental motifs. The antique from which it was copied was made about 1760-70 and used to line a trunk. Sold in double rolls.

Single roll 7 yds x 20''; repeat 22''

EDENTON

This elegant pattern is a copy of antique wallpaper found in the Joseph Hewes House, Edenton, North Carolina. The design was printed in the first quarter of the nineteenth century, and the reproduction is available only in the document color shown.
A formal wallpaper that shows up smartly in a hallway or dining room. Sold in double rolls.

Single roll 7⅞ yds x 20″; repeat 40″

DUKE OF GLOUCESTER

Three sources contributed to this commemorative pattern. The vase and flowers were inspired by the lush floral arrangements used in the Governor's Palace, and the birds were copied from the Chinese wallpaper in the Palace supper room. The overall pattern is based on an eighteenth-century English textile. The result: a wall covering of great elegance. Sold in double rolls.

Single roll 7 yds x 20″; repeat 22″

Williamsburg in a traditional room. This comfortable conversational setting reveals the timeless beauty of eighteenth-century furnishings in today's home. The Chippendale sofa is 39174, the two side chairs are 39067 and the tea table is 39008.

FABRICS
BY SCHUMACHER

More than 61 different patterns in some 300 color variations make up the collection of Williamsburg Fabrics produced for Craft House exclusively by F. Schumacher and Company of New York. While most of these are authentic reproductions of antique textiles used in Colonial Williamsburg, some are commemorative patterns highlighting the life and art of eighteenth-century Williamsburg.

The bold colors, rich patterns, and lush textures of these fine fabrics reveal the vitality of this exciting period.

This amazingly versatile fabric collection offers a means of giving any home, however contemporary it may be, some of the charm of Williamsburg's restored houses and public buildings. An infinite number of combinations and colors is possible, and the name Schumacher, like the hallmark of Williamsburg Reproductions, has always symbolized quality.

Color samples of all Williamsburg fabrics are available upon request: cotton samples (4" x 6") fifty cents per pattern with full color range included; damask samples (3" x 6") $1.00 deposit per sample. Large samples of all fabrics are also available on a loan basis; a deposit equivalent to the price per yard is requested. All deposits are refunded when samples are returned.

WYTHE HOUSE BORDER RESIST

This fine cotton fabric, resist-dyed in two shades of blue, is shown here as it is used in a bedroom of the George Wythe House. Its striking pattern repeat of large leaves and sunflowers, with a two-inch border of trailing vines, has been copied from a mid-eighteenth-century textile. Note the use of the contrasting border to outline draperies and valances in this set of window and bed hangings.

Width 50"; repeat 28".

All fabrics are available in a choice of colors.

HERRINGBONE STRIE

This silk and cotton strie is a lovely complimentary fabric. An adaptation of a fabric woven during the eighteenth century. It will easily blend with its coordinating fabric, Herringbone Stripe, as well as with a host of other textiles.

Width 50″.

HERRINGBONE STRIPE

The original bourette from the last half of the eighteenth century is woven in alternating stripes within a herringbone weave. Adaptation color ways have been developed which will enhance a variety of color schemes.

Width 50″.

BOTANICAL CHINTZ

A bold design gives this cotton print its stylistic character. Reproduced from a late eighteenth century French fabric, the numerous colors make this fabric a versatile accessory.

Width 54″; repeat 26¾″.

131

LOZENGE FLORAL

Polychrome flower bouquets framed by a lozenge pattern of entwining vines give this cotton fabric a light and airy feeling. By adding a delicate touch to upholstery or a window treatment it can complement both an informal or formal setting. The original textile is a French block printed cotton dating from about 1770. The fabric shown with it is Wicker Velverette. See page 137.

Width 54″; repeat 14″.

CHINESE FLOWERS

This distinctive cotton fabric uses twelve colors during its printing process. Adapted from a Chinese hand painted gauze made for the English market about 1760, this fabric captures the elegance and beauty of the original. The accompanying fabric is Williamsburg Wool shown on page 135.

Width 54″; repeat 27″.

TRACERY FLORAL

In a number of stunning color ways this cotton fabric's hearty design will hold its own. By using it as your focal point, a range of complimentary colors can be chosen to enliven your room scheme.

Width 54″; repeat 13″.

MORNING GLORY

The monochromatic colors in this reproduction faithfully illustrate the character of the French chintz of circa 1775, which this cotton reproduces. The striking floral and stripe design creates a refined pattern, typical of the period. Related wallpaper on page 117. The paint color is Brush-Everard Blue.

Width 54″; repeat 36¼″.

FLOWER LEAF STRIPE

The original fabric used as a quilt backing is French and dates from the late eighteenth century. The charming reproduction with a linear flower motif demonstrates the adaptability in cotton of eighteenth-century design for today's needs.

Width 54″; repeat 10″.

CHINESE BELLS

The original late eighteenth century blocked printed fabric is French. The chinoisere design of this reproduction cotton fabric illustrates the global fascination with the Orient in the eighteenth century. This tasteful motif is still applicable for today's decorating needs. Shown here with Bruton Adaptation Damask. Page 139.

Width 54″; repeat 28″.

PILLEMENT
This cotton fabric is a reproduction of a French block printed textile. The original is in the style of Jean Pillement, a French engraver-designer during the eighteenth and early nineteenth centuries.

Width 48"; repeat 16".

PARSLEY
A versatile cotton that can be used in a multitude of ways. Reproduced from a pattern swatchbook, circa 1800, this design proves itself to be timeless.

Width 54"; repeat 16".

PINEAPPLE & POPPY
The original fabric is a chintz probably printed circa 1800 in Alsace, France. The robust design is suitable in a large room which demands a fabric of visual integrity.

Width 64"; repeat 25¼".

BANYAN PRINT

An Indian chintz dressing gown or banyan is the document from which this textile is reproduced. The delicate meandering vines and flowers produce a design on cotton that is visually pleasing.

Width 54″; repeat 18″.

WILLIAMSBURG WOOL

This solid color wool fabric is both attractive and durable. The English original was woven in the early eighteenth century. The chair is 39013.

Width 54″.

SPRING FLOWERS

A naturalistic rendering of tulips, marigolds, primroses and columbines gives this reproduction fabric a graceful appearance not easily duplicated. The cotton fabric comes in an assortment of adaptation colors. The paint color is Brush-Everard Blue.

Width 54″; repeat 22″.

STRING OF PEARLS

The graceful motif of this reproduction cotton fabric comes from an eighteenth century French block-print. It faithfully reproduces the meandering pearls and floral designs.

Width 54″; repeat 35″.

CALICO BIRD

This wallpaper's pattern came from a late eighteenth or early nineteenth century French textile. Its whimsical charm and delightful colors would create a beautiful setting for anyone young at heart. Related wallpaper may be seen on page 110. The paint is Powell-Waller Red.

Width 54″; repeat 14″.

WICKER VELVERETTE

This cotton printed reproduction takes its design source from a textile swatch-book. The book is probably from the firm of Thomas Smith in Manchester, England and was used by merchants and customers to choose the fabrics they wanted to order from England. The small repetitive motif appears modern in inspiration, but dates from the late eighteenth century.

Width 54″.

CHINESE PEONY

A brilliant Chinese lacquer-red silk damask was the original from which this dramatic fabric was copied. Made in China about 1745, the pattern is an offset repeat of peonies and scrolling leaves with small Chinese symbols interspersed.

Width 54″; repeat 16¾″.

WYTHE HOUSE FLORAL

This fine cotton fabric is a delightful combination of two eighteenth-century textile designs. An overall pattern of thorny stems bearing numerous flowers, leaves, and buds, is teamed with slender side borders of alternate flowers and stripes. Look for the related wallpaper on page 123. The paint color is Bassett Hall Antique Gold.

Width 48″; repeat 13¾″.

137

LIVERPOOL BIRDS

Two popular eighteenth-century motifs, stripes and fanciful birds, are combined in this fine cotton fabric. A stripe of exotic, imaginary birds is alternated with a plain stripe.

Width 52″; repeat 7″.

ANTHESIS

This printed cotton fabric with its dramatic design of chrysanthemums, birds and branches has been copied from an English polychrome woodblock print of about 1780.

Width 54″; repeat 32″.

GREEN SPRING DAMASK

A compact, symmetrical design of tulips, lilies, and carnations with fanciful leaves forms the motif of this elegant silk damask. The original fabric is mid-seventeenth-century Italian. Also available as a silk and cotton adaptation fabric.
Silk: width 54″; repeat 8½″.
Silk and rayon: width 54″; repeat 8″.

LUDWELL DAMASK

A central framed bouquet highlights the woven floral pattern of this elegant damask. Blue, the document color of this early-to-mid-eighteenth-century design, is reproduced on pure silk; adaptation colors, including the color shown, are in cotton. The chair is 39304.

Silk (blue only): width 50"; repeat 17½".
Cotton: width 53"; repeat 18½".

BRUTON DAMASK

Highlight of this rich silk fabric is a repeating central design of graceful flowers framed in a foliate cartouche. This fine damask is also available as an adaptation fabric in silk and cotton.

Silk: width 50"; repeat 23½".
Silk and cotton: width 52"; repeat 21¼".

LINER STRIPE*
This delicate design of stripes printed
on 100% cotton is copied from the
border tape used on antique bed hangings in the James Geddy House. The
related wallpaper is on page 125.
The paint color is Brafferton Blue.

Width 50".

PLEASURES OF THE FARM
Charming rural scenes of eighteenth-
century France are illustrated in great
detail in this fine printed cotton. It is
a reproduction of a French toile de
Jouy, copperplate-printed about 1783;
a delightful choice for an eighteenth-
century look in living room or dining
room. The sofa is 38005.

Width 40"; repeat 40".

HORSE AND FOX

A Wythe House bedroom is the showcase for this interesting reproduction of a design first printed in England about 1770. Animal vignettes are set among winding branches of a tree in this fine cotton fabric. Shown here with Williamsburg Wool. Page 135.

Width 36"; repeat 37".

TAVERN CHECK

This striking linen and cotton fabric brings the hospitable spirit of Williamsburg inns and taverns to your family room or breakfast room. Its bold checks were copied from an American antique. The related wallpaper is on page 126.

Width 48"; repeat 3".

FLORAL STRIPE

This reproduction of an eighteenth-century French textile alternates dainty ribbon-looped bouquets with wide stripes of stylized flowers. This charming cotton fabric has its related wallpaper, as shown on page 122. The paint color is Daphne Room Beige.

Width 32"; repeat 12½".

JONES TOILE

An English textile, made in 1761 by Robert Jones in his Old Ford factory in London, is reproduced in printed cotton used as bed hangings in the Chamber over the Dining Room of the Governor's Palace. The legends "R. Jones/1761" and "R.I.&Co./Old Ford/1761" form an unobtrusive part of the design. The color related wallpaper is Multistripe, page 122. The paint is Brown House Beige.

Width 40″; repeat 77″.

FLOWERED PRINT

This bright cotton was reproduced from an antique French textile, circa 1780. Its overall design of vine-like stems bearing berries, leaves, and exotic flowers is copied in a related wallpaper described on page 114.

Width 36″; repeat 14½″.

BRUTON RESIST

Stylized chrysanthemums, lilacs and graceful fern-like leaves create a striking pattern on this linen and cotton fabric reproduced from an eighteenth century textile. A related wallpaper may be seen on page 124.

Width 54″; repeat 13″.

APPLES

These stylized apples and narrow stripes on a natural background have been copied from an eighteenth-century quilt lining. The pattern has been reproduced in linen and adapted in a woven cotton. Related wallpaper is shown on page 115.

†Woven cotton: width 54″.
Printed linen: width 48″.

The 39304 and 38047 chairs are covered in Ludwell Adaptation Damask.

DIAMOND FLORAL

Originally from Provence in France, this restrained but lively pattern bespeaks continental European influences on eighteenth-century England and her American colonies. It suggests many contemporary usages. The related wallpaper is on page 119. Brafferton Blue is the complementary paint color.

Width 54″; repeat 8″.

FLEURETTE

Small isolated symmetrical flower motifs in offset alignment adorn this damask copied from the silk antique of about 1800. Small repetitive patterned silks of this type were used for clothing as well as furnishings.

Silk: Width 54″; repeat 3½″.

Silk and Rayon: Width 54″; repeat 3½″.

WILLIAMSBURG STRIPE

Stripes of varying widths are woven in dramatic colors to create this luxurious silk and cotton fabric. A copy of an eighteenth-century Italian antique, it makes a striking addition to contemporary decor. Related wallpaper on page 125.

Width 50″.

GRAPES

One of the oldest and most popular of the Williamsburg reproduction fabrics, this cotton has stripes of grapes, vines, and leaves, alternating with a stripe of small flower-and-leaf design. The original is English, block-printed about 1790. The color related fabric is Herringbone Strie. See page 131.

Width 54"; repeat 17".

SCOTCH CLOTH

Reproduced in wool from a "Scotch" carpet design, it is also available as a 100% cotton adaptation that beautifully re-creates the integrity of the original. The fabric will easily cover your upholstered items with a lasting beauty.

Wool: width 50"; repeat 2¼".

Cotton: width 50"; repeat 2¼".

PONDICHERRY
Delicate trailing vines and flowers inspired the airy design for this fine
cotton fabric. The eighteenth-century
example from which it is copied is an
Indian mordant painted cotton. A
related wallpaper is shown on page 118.
The paint is Redlion Inn Green.

Width 54"; repeat 17¼".

WYTHE HOUSE STRIPE
One is reminded of the gracious atmosphere of the Wythe House in this
simple yet elegant cotton fabric. Two-
tone red is the document color, with
many other colors available. Illustrated
here with color related Jones Toile. See
page 142.

Width 50".

JARDIN CHINOIS
Reproduced in exacting detail from
a quilt fragment in the Colonial
Williamsburg textile collection, this
block print dates from the period 1760-
1780. The chinoiserie pattern of
gazebos and floral sprigs reflects the
Chinese influence popular at the time.
The paint color is Prentis Store Gray
Green.

Width 54"; repeat 13".

FLOWERING TREE
Bring Williamsburg charm to chairs, sofa, or draperies with this colorful glazed chintz copied from an antique English quilt. Its repeating pattern shows branches bearing peonies, roses, tulips and poppies as well as a variety of leaves.

Width 54″; repeat 34″.

INDIAN FLOWERS
Exotic flowers, fruit and leaves in vivid colors on natural cotton are typical of the mordant-painted and dyed fabrics popularized in Europe during the late eighteenth-century by the East India trade.

Width 54″; repeat 12¼″.

PLANTATION CALICO
Indian designs of exotic plants and flowers influenced this charming pattern, copied from a French document of the late eighteenth century. The fine cotton fabric would harmonize with French Provincial or eighteenth-century English style furniture.

Width 50″; repeat 13¼″.

DOBBY WEAVE
A versatile solid-color cotton fabric, Dobby Weave is a copy of an American woven diaper design. It is available in a wide range of fresh colors, all treated with stain-resistant Zepel to make them practical in any home.

Width 54".

WOOD FLORAL
The bold and attractive design of flowers and foliage set against a dotted background is taken from a French printed cotton used in a coverlet made in the last decade of the eighteenth century. The reproduction is also cotton.

Width 54"; repeat 16".

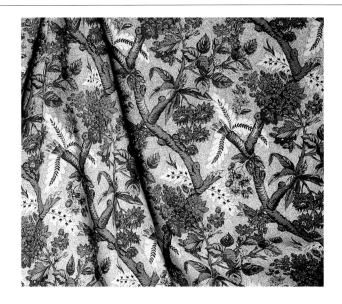

STENCIL FLOWERS
An eighteenth-century resist-dyed textile of indigo and white with alternating columns of flowers and vines has been reproduced in a wide range of rich colors on this linen and cotton fabric. The related wallpaper is illustrated on page 118.

Width 54"; repeat 12½".

RALEIGH TAVERN RESIST
Adapted from an antique French design, resist-dyed, this linen and cotton fabric has a pattern of stylized floral bouquets alternating with a ribbon entwined with fruit and flowers. Its related wallpaper is described on page 121.

Width 50″; repeat 42″.

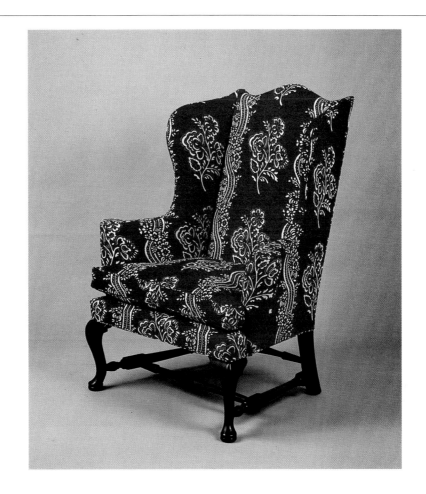

POMEGRANATE RESIST
A spectacular design of large pomegranate flowers and feathery leaves, copied from an eighteenth-century resist-dyed textile, distinguishes this linen and cotton fabric.

Width 50″; repeat 20½″.

149

TULIP
Dainty stylized tulips in neat geometric arrangement make up this attractive woven cotton fabric. The design, derived from a seventeenth-century document, has its related wallpaper pictured on page 121.

Width 54".

PINTADO STRIPE
Like so many fine cottons, this is of East Indian origin; its Indian name means painted cotton. Light and airy, the design comes from an antique cotton fabric, probably French, made about 1775. The reproduction is 100% cotton. A related wallpaper is shown on page 115. The paint color is Daphne Room Beige.

Width 36".

MULTI-STRIPE
Stripes were the fashion in the late eighteenth century, as demonstrated by this handsome chevron twill design on cotton. Related wallpaper by Katzenback and Warren on page 122. The paint color is Powell-Waller Red.

Width 50".

WILLIAMSBURG IRIS

A crisp, flowing print with a large repeat decorates this cotton fabric copied from the English copperplate-printed original of about 1780. The paint color is Powell-Waller Red. A related wallpaper is shown on page 111. This design also appears as a dinnerware pattern. See page 220.

Width 54½″; repeat 36½″.

SHIR-O-SHAKKAR

This is the original East Indian name for seersucker, which literally meant "milk and sugar." Alternating plain and puckered stripes of 100% cotton make a simple, yet unusual fabric that would brighten any room. Shown here with a William and Mary Bedspread, page 156.

Width 54″.

POTPOURRI

This popular reproduction fabric displays a gay medley of flowers and leaves, spiced with color. It is copied from a piece of antique block-printed cotton nade in England. Related dinnerware by Wedgwood and wallpaper by Katzenbach and Warren are also available (pages 121 and 220).

Width 36″; repeat 22¼″.
Width 54″; repeat 26¼″.

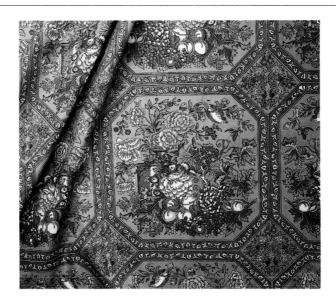

FLORAL TRAILS

A design reminiscent of needlework enhances this fine cotton, suitable for bedroom or sitting room. Like the original, copperplate-printed in England about 1770, the fabric has graceful vines bearing roses, daisies, crocuses, bachelor's buttons, lilies and thistles. The paint is Brush-Everard Blue.

Width 54"; repeat 32".

EDINBURGH CHECK

The checked pattern of this linen fabric is copied from eighteenth-century bed hangings made in New England from a textile probably woven in Scotland. Checks were among the most popular furnishing fabrics for upholstery, curtains, and bed hangings throughout the eighteenth century. The paint is Powell-Waller Red. A related wallpaper is on page 112.

Width 48".

BLUEBELL STRIPE

An English block-printed design of about 1770 inspired this delicate design which alternates a trailing vine of bluebells with a stripe of diamond shapes. The reproduction is treated with stain-resistant Zepel for modern practicality. The related wallpaper is shown on page 113.

Width 54".

CHECKS

Always in fashion, always adaptable to any environment, this small checked linen and cotton fabric is reproduced from an American antique document. Related wallpaper is described on page 124.

Width 48".

Above: 39012 wing chair, 39167 table and 38012 wing chair.

Williamsburg ®

FRINGES
BY F. SCHUMACHER AND COMPANY

Inspired by the fringes in the Colonial Williamsburg collection, F. Schumacher and Company have introduced an initial group of seven adaptation fringes. These patterns are derived from the handmade originals and represent a diversity of styles in use during the eighteenth and early nineteenth centuries. These trimmings are offered in a wide range of colors for use with Williamsburg fabrics and to provide the authentic finishing touch for a wide variety of period or contemporary window treatments and bedhangings.

Color samples of all styles and colors of Williamsburg fringes are available upon request. A deposit of $1.00 each is requested. All deposits are refunded when samples are returned.

The simple elegance of Tassel Fringe complements the fabric Liverpool Birds in this window treatment.

SCALLOP FRINGE
A narrow finishing fringe with a scalloped pattern of looped threads. Approximately 1″ deep 100% Cotton.

TASSEL FRINGE
A fringe with a light and airy appearance. Approximately 2½″ deep. 100% Cotton.

TWISTED FRINGE
A simply styled fringe, straight-cut and twisted. Approximately 2½″ deep. 100% Cotton.

UNEVEN TASSEL FRINGE
An elegant scalloped tassel fringe. Approximately 2½″ deep. 100% Rayon.

FANCY CUT FRINGE
A deep straight fringe with a wide woven heading. Approximately 3½″ deep. 100% Cotton.

SCALLOP FRINGE
A scalloped style with looped threads. Approximately 2″ deep. 100% Silk.

STRAIGHT CUT FRINGE
This attractive fringe was used for the bedhangings on page 00. Approximately 2½″ deep. 67% Wool, 33% Cotton.

Scallop Fringe

Tassel Fringe

Twisted Fringe

Uneven Tassel Fringe

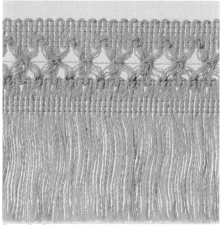
Fancy Cut Fringe

Scallop Fringe

Straight Cut Fringe

155

Williamsburg®

BEDSPREADS
BY BATES FABRICS INC.

Bates Fabrics Inc., weavers and printers of fine quality textiles, have reproduced for Craft House three beautiful bedspreads in different textiles and a wide selection of exciting contemporary colors. These versatile reproductions are as at home in today's contemporary settings as the originals were in the eighteenth century.

WYTHE HOUSE

Copied from a coverlet thought to have been made in Virginia, this bedspread of 100% cotton suggests the overshot patterns popular in the eighteenth and nineteenth centuries. It can be machine washed and dried with no pressing required. It comes in a gift box in the following sizes and colors:

Twin: 80″ x 110″
Double: 96″ x 110″

Colors: Snow White, Antique White, Green, Red, Russet, Ochre, Gold, Blue.

WILLIAM AND MARY

Mythological birds and animals, combined with large symmetrical leaf and plant motifs, provide the distinguished border design of this copy of a late seventeenth-century quilted coverlet. The center portion has an all-over diamond pattern. Of 100% cotton, this bedspread can be machine washed and dried with no pressing necessary. It is available in the following sizes and colors:

Twin: 80″ x 110″
Double: 96″ x 110″

Colors: Snow White, Antique White.

MARSEILLES

Giving the effect of quilting, this reproduction matelasse bedspread is styled after a loom-woven counterpane probably made in France about 1820. In the early nineteenth century this type of counterpane was called "Marseilles." The fringe is double-knotted string. Of 100% cotton, the spread can be machine-washed and dried, with no pressing required. It is available in a gift box in the following sizes and colors:

Twin: 80" x 114"
Double: 96" x 114"

Colors: Gold, Antique White, Antique Blue, Antique Green, Snow White.

Color samples of Williamsburg bedspreads are available upon request. A $1.00 deposit is requested for each pattern. All deposits are refunded when samples are returned.

BLANKET, HEAVY WEIGHT
A single charcoal band of color at the end of this heavy weight blanket adds that certain touch of classic design. The original handwoven blanket, circa 1800, is from either England or America.

21708 Twin 71" x 91"
21709 Double 79" x 91"
21710 Queen 91" x 91"
21711 King 110" x 91"

BLANKET, LIGHT WEIGHT
The lovely reproduction captures the light texture of the original blanket, probably made in America during the eighteenth century. Its light weight makes it a necessity on cool autumn evenings.

21700 Twin 71" x 91"
21701 Double 79" x 91"
21702 Queen 91" x 91"
21703 King 110" x 91"

BLANKET, MEDIUM WEIGHT
The original of this blanket was probably made in St. Mary's County, Maryland, in the late eighteenth century. The creamy white color with the red graduated border gives this blanket a country feeling so popular today.

21704 Twin 71" x 91"
21705 Double 79" x 91"
21706 Queen 91" x 91"
21707 King 110" x 91"

21708

21700

21704

CLOCKS-MIRRORS-PRINTS-LIGHTING FIXTURES

In April, 1757, George Washington ordered merchandise from his agent in London and instructed, "... let them be fashionable, neat, and good in their several kinds ..." Today's aware consumer seeks the same high quality in home furnishings and finds it beautifully expressed in reproduction clocks, mirrors, prints, and lighting fixtures from Williamsburg.

Perhaps more than any other single item of household furnishing, a clock adds a feeling of life to a room. Whether it's the discreet ticking of a shelf or wall clock or the resonant chime of a tall case clock, these important pieces mark the passage of time and of generations, for these are indeed heirlooms for the future.

A fine clock has a quiet dignity. Its unparalleled combination of beauty and usefulness seems to speak of lasting values that have endured through the ages. In today's sometime hectic world, a Williamsburg clock regulates our comings and goings and punctuates the important events of our lives.

Tall case clocks came into being following the introduction of the pendulum in the middle of the seventeenth century. This method of regulation marked a most important development in the science of measuring time. Prior to that time clocks were generally weight driven and wall mounted, with adequate space below being necessary to accommodate the fall of the weights. With the advent of the long pendulum, clock cases could be free standing and quickly gained importance as decorative pieces of furniture. The long case was originally designed to protect the mechanism from outside interference, but soon the clockmaker was using all his skills to make it as beautiful as it was practical. When short pendulums were introduced in England about 1658, smaller clocks were possible and table and shelf clocks began to appear.

From the Kittinger Company of Buffalo, New York, comes an outstanding group of stately tall case clocks reproduced from fine examples in the collection at Williamsburg. One, the Lord Dunmore clock, is copied from an antique owned by the last royal governor of Virginia who left it behind when he fled the colony to escape the impending American Revolution.

The nineteenth century produced several prominent clockmakers whose names have come to be associated with fine shelf and wall clocks. The Chelsea Clock Company of Chelsea, Massachusetts, has carefully reproduced fine examples of two of these well known craftsmen. The Terry clock, rectangular in form, is a superb focal point for a mantel, while the interesting contours of the Willard banjo clock add interest to a wall.

All Williamsburg clocks exemplify fine cabinetry and precision made movements. The warrant which Eli Terry affixed to his clock is equally applicable to each of these reproductions: "The public may be assured that this kind of clock will run as long without repairs, and be as durable and accurate for keeping time, as any kind of clock whatsoever."

Mirrors were another decorative wonder in the eighteenth century, for only quite recently had it become possible to fabricate large pieces of plate glass.

For the first time craftsmen were free to lavish their skills on mirrors of great size, and their products symbolized the newest in wealth and luxury. To this day, mirrors provide a superb addition to any decor. They are things of beauty in themselves, and, properly used, they add depth or dimension to a room, increase the natural lighting, reflect artificial light and objects, and duplicate architectural details.

With mirrors from the Colonial Williamsburg collection one can reproduce in a modern setting the effects that the eighteenth century strove for, and obtained, in its handsome rooms.

Colonial Williamsburg owns and displays magnificent period mirrors in their traditional settings— "looking glasses" as they were aptly termed. Selections of these

Mirrors from wood carvings and a very special compo with 22 carat gold burnished to a high sheen with an agate. Convex and beveled edged mirrors—two-part mirrors that are matches of the antiques.

antiques are available as reproductions and adaptations by Friedman Brothers Decorative Arts of Medley, Florida. Great care has been taken with the details: beveled edges are appropriately heavy and the inclination just right. Gilded designs on lacquered frames are subtle and delicate (a skill that few master). Because of this attention to precision, the Williamsburg mirrors of today are successful reflections of their ancestors. This is a task not easily, but admirably, accomplished. The beauty of these mirrors is in design, the pleasure is unlimited use.

Smaller ones may be hung over a chest of drawers or a dressing table, or simply displayed as an incidental piece in a hallway. Also, such a mirror serves handsomely for shaving in a man's dressing room. The complexity of a picture wall can be relieved by the addition of a simple looking glass, while mirrors of larger dimensions can become a major accent piece on a wall or over a mantel.

Examples begin with Queen Anne and follow the changing styles throughout the century. Wall mirrors faithfully reflected the changing times, as well as the furniture styles of the periods.

There is no doubt that the walls of eighteenth-century rooms were decorated with contemporary prints, engravings, and maps. The Dietz Press of Richmond, Virginia, publishes a superb series of reproductions of early eighteenth-century hand-tinted prints originally prepared by the English naturalist Mark Catesby and the English nurseryman Robert Furber (flowers and fruits). These original prints of Catesby and Furber were valued in their time and are rare today. Although Robert Furber did not visit Virginia, Mark Catesby traveled widely and lived in Williamsburg between 1712 and 1717. All of these prints are exquisite in detail and add an elegant touch to a formal or semi-formal setting. They become the small but important things that "make the past alive."

Colonial Williamsburg has commissioned noted present-day artists to capture the moods of Williamsburg. Included in this group is a superb series of limited edition bird prints, etchings of Williamsburg buildings great and small, and a series depicting taverns and changing seasons.

The eighteenth century depended on candlelight after dark. But it did so in its own special style with gracious chandeliers, hanging lanterns, sconces, hurricane lamps and carriage lanterns. These fixtures, in brass, tin, pewter, and copper, are reproductions created by Virginia Metalcrafters of Waynesboro, Virginia.

Available for use with candles (which have their own modern vogue), or wired for electric lighting.

Table lamps, of course, were unknown to eighteenth-century homeowners. Today we choose them to light traditional and contemporary rooms with distinction. Williamsburg adaptation lamps offer the solution to this often hard-to-find accessory. Favorite candlesticks and vases, whose designs are strong enough to accommodate the addition of hardware and shades, add drama as well as light. They are, in a way, extensions of the antiques that the eighteenth-century craftsman would surely approve, for he always sought new ways to make his products fashionable, neat, and good.

Fruit and Floral prints, Fish and Bird prints meticulously hand-colored. Mirrors and chairs decorated by hand—as were their antique counterparts now in the Colonial Williamsburg collection.

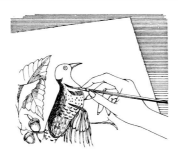

MOODY HOUSE CLOCK 39736

This remarkable tall case clock is a superb reproduction of an early nineteenth-century antique located in the Moody House at Colonial Williamsburg. Constructed of mahogany with crotch mahogany veneer on its door frame and base, the "Moody House Clock" incorporates the lighter scaled moldings and detailing typical of the early nineteenth century. The New England styling is enhanced by a graceful swan neck pediment.

The movement for the clock is precision made in America using the finest materials and highest quality workmanship obtainable. It features an eight-day hourly bell strike, typical of those used in fine clocks dating from the eighteenth century. The unusual care taken in construction results in parts that are very resistant to wear and a pendulum movement that is exceptionally accurate. The bell is handcast of a hardened bronze alloy to achieve the dignified tone of the antique clock.

The detailed dial on the "Moody House Clock" is handpainted. It features unusual alternating colored spandrels, 23-carat gold decoration, and a 31-day calendar wheel. The moon dial is flanked by global maps and the moving moon phases alternate with ship and cottage scenes.

All of the enduring beauty and charm of the antique have been captured by craftsmen at the Kittinger Company in this reproduction. It is certain to occupy a position of prominence in the most fashionable homes and offices, just as the antique does in the Moody House at Colonial Williamsburg.

Height 96⅞"; width 20⅞"; depth 10¼".

THE LORD DUNMORE CLOCK 39730

Colonial Williamsburg and the Kittinger Company take particular pride in presenting the Lord Dunmore Clock, reproduced from an antique once owned by the last royal governor of the colony of Virginia.

Several years ago, expert craftsmen of the Kittinger Company began the meticulous, painstaking process of reproducing this extraordinary clock. The result, pictured here, is a benchmark in Kittinger's long history of offering quality that is second to none.

The case of the clock, styled in the neat, plain fashion popular in the late 1760s and early 1770s, is crafted of fine mahogany and, like the original, is constructed in two parts. The removable hood slides forward to expose the movement. The distinctive mellow patina of the heirloom finish is achieved by a handfinishing process that requires six weeks and twenty-one separate steps to complete. Polished brass finials accent the corners and graceful pediment of the hood.

The dial features a silvered brass chapter ring with etched and filled Roman hour numerals and Arabic minute numerals. Rococo spandrels in the corners and flanking the strike-silent ring are of cast brass. An inverted scalloped edge borders an inset silvered seconds dial. Delicately cut hour and minute hands are made identical with the antique, and the winding key is solid brass.

The American-made movement is an eight-day hourly bell strike typical of those used in fine clocks dating from the early eighteenth century. The short-swing pendulum assembly has a steel rod and lead-filled brass bob. The bell is handcast of a hardened bronze alloy to achieve the tone of the antique.

Height 94½"; width 20⅛"; depth 10½".

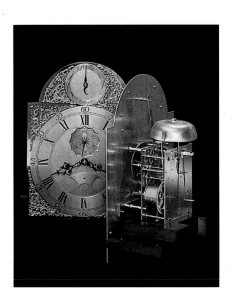

WETHERBURN TAVERN CLOCK 39733

A faithful mahogany reproduction of the original made in Pennsylvania, the design of its case is straightforward, reflecting English design of the early eighteenth century. Its well-constructed case is typical of back country Pennsylvania cabinetwork. It has a brass and silvered brass dial and an eight-day hourly bell strike movement.

Height 86¼″; width 20¾″; depth 11¼″.

WYTHE HOUSE CLOCK

The Wythe House Clock is an authentic reproduction of a late eighteenth-century English clock in the George Wythe House. Its hand-rubbed solid mahogany cabinet is enriched with an inlaid design of holly wood. The feet, face-frame, and top handle are of solid brass. Modern mechanisms are of the finest quality. Height (with handle extended) 10½"; width 7½"; depth 4"; diameter of dial 3⅞".

35700 Wythe House Clock, striking
35701 Wythe House Clock, non-striking

MANTEL CLOCK 35704

E. Terry & Sons were well known clock-makers during the early nineteenth century. This clock, an accurate reproduction of the original with reverse painting on glass has a history of ownership in Williamsburg, would handsomely adorn your mantle or shelf. The movement by Chelsea Clock Co. is gold plated.

Height 31"; width 17¼"; depth 4½".

BANJO WALL CLOCK 35707

Banjo clocks were a stylish adornment in homes, when the 1820 original of this clock was made in Boston. The highly decorative case of this clock with reverse painting on glass, illustrates Americans' love of adornment during this period, as well as the continued use of patriotic motifs. The eagle is 22k gold. Chelsea Clock Co. reproduced this handsome clock.

Height 33"; width 10¾". depth 4½".

35704

35707

The gardener's workshop at the Brush-Everard House.

Williamsburg ®

MIRRORS
BY FRIEDMAN BROTHERS
DECORATIVE ARTS

The decorative value of mirrors has been known and artfully used since the Middle Ages. Once a status symbol of great wealth and luxury, these "looking glasses" were sometimes used to line an entire wall or room.

Today's homemaker is even more inventive. She knows the space expanding value of a mirror, and its subtle touch of doubling the beauty of a flower arrangement or unusual accessory by reflection. A mirror adds life and sparkle wherever it is used.

Included in this selection of Williamsburg Mirror Reproductions by Friedman Brothers are examples of the more elaborate as well as the simpler styles of the colonial period. The originals hang in the restored buildings of Colonial Williamsburg. The copies have been faithfully reproduced by master craftsmen.

59007
This two-plate mirror of the Queen Anne period is enhanced by the black lacquer frame, richly decorated with Chinese birds and plants. The original, made in England about 1715, can be seen today in the West Advance Building of the Governor's Palace. This mirror is also available with a red or green lacquer frame.

Glass 15" x 44¼"; overall size is 18¾" x 48".

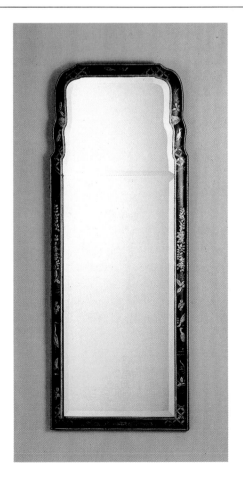

Williamsburg ®

Looking glasses, as mirrors were called in the eighteenth century, were highly prized possessions during the early days of the colonies. Few mirrors were made here, therefore the glass had to be shipped from England at great expense.

59016
This reproduction mirror adheres to the strong baroque architectural quality of the original. Available in either gold leaf (59016) or gold metal leaf (59916).

Height 51¾"; weight 24¾"; depth 1¼".

The English original of this piece is in the Pantry of the Governor's Palace and dates from 1725-1740.

59016

59014
Fanciful gilded chinoiserie figures and flowers decorate the lacquered frame of this strikingly beautiful Queen Anne mirror. The eighteenth-century American original now hangs in the hallway of the Peyton Randolph House. It is available with a red, green or black lacquer frame.

Glass 34⅜" x 15⅜";
overall size 44" x 18¼".

59004
This two-plate mirror is a handsome example of the long Queen Anne looking glasses, with gilded birds and plant life applied on the black lacquered frame. Use it in a foyer or in the dining room over a sideboard.
The original was made about 1715 in England. It is available with a red, green, or black lacquer frame.

Glass 14½" x 39½";
overall size 18" x 43".

59014

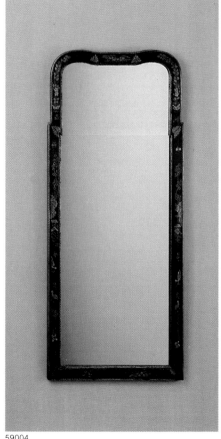

59004

59167

This elaborate mirror was adapted from a mid-eighteenth century English looking glass now hanging in the Lightfoot House. The glass is surrounded by a pierced gilt frame that incorporates scrolls, ruffles, foliage and swags of fruit.

Glass 20″ x 28¾″; overall size 26½″ x 46″.

59128

This pleasing simplicity of this Queen Anne mirror faithfully retains the feeling of the original piece, made in England about 1710 and now in the Williamsburg collection. Available with either mahogany or gold frame. Beveled glass optional.

Glass 21¼″ x 29½″; overall size 23½″ x 31½″.

59167

59128

The clean, simple lines of these graceful Queen Anne mirrors add their gracious touch to a variety of settings, blending smoothly with modern designs as well as more traditional ones. They are exact copies of English antiques, made about 1725 and may now be seen in the Peyton Randolph House and the George Wythe House. The glass is beveled to follow the delicate lines of the frame in these fine reproductions. Both are available as wall mirrors, or with an easel back for use on a dressing table or chest of drawers.

59910 Hanging Mirror and 59010 Easel Mirror. Frame available in either polished or antique gold.

Glass 15″ x 21¼″; overall size 15¾″ x 22″.

59911 Hanging Mirror and 59011 Easel Mirror in antique gold or polished gold frame.

59802 Hanging Mirror and 59801 Easel Mirror in black frame.

Glass 13¼″ x 23¼″; overall size 14¾″ x 24¾″.

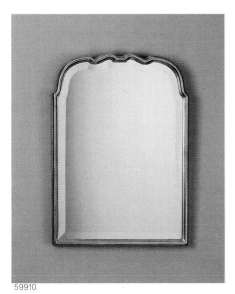

59910

59911

59801

167

59002

This eye-catching piece would make a delightfully different focal point for a wall gallery. The Federal-style mirror has convex glass, and is framed in gilt wood and gesso. Two candle arms balance a fiery eagle with outspread arms. The original was probably made in America in the early nineteenth century, and now hangs in the Williamsburg Inn. Available in either gold leaf (59002) or gold metal leaf (59002).

Glass diameter 11¾";
overall size 17½" x 38¾".

59003

This Adam-style mirror, with its intricately detailed ornamentation, is a copy of a late-eighteenth century antique. The oval glass is framed in gold leaf with an elaborate design of urn, flowers and leaves. Available in either gold leaf (59003) or gold metal leaf (59903).

Glass 15½" x 25½";
overall size 22" x 49½".

59002

59003

59015

This ornate mirror is a careful copy of an English antique that was made about 1740. Because of the intricate gilt and gesso details, this mirror deserves a prominent place in the home. It could easily be hung in a master bedroom or dressing room as well as the dining room. It is made of the finest walnut and walnut veneer. Available in either gold leaf (59015) or gold metal leaf (59915).

Glass 22" x 34";
overall size 28½" x 58".

59006

This magnificent Queen Anne looking glass is a faithfull copy of an original dating from the reign of George I and now in Wetherburn's Tavern. The entire frame is made of rich gilded gesso, and is decorated with a carved shell and two eagle heads. Available in either gold leaf (59006) or gold metal leaf (59906).

Glass 16½" x 28½";
overall size 22¼" x 41".

59015

59006

59005
This Georgian mirror is framed in delicately carved burl walnut, adorned with Prince of Wales feathers in gold leaf. The original was made in England between 1740 and 1750.

Glass 20¼″ x 27¼″;
overall size 28¾″ x 46½″.

59008
This delicate Chippendale mirror is framed in mahogany, with a gilded rosette of stylized leaves. It is an exact copy of the original, which was made in England about 1760, and now hangs in the King's Arms Tavern in Williamsburg.

Glass 15½″ x 27¼″;
overall size 22″ x 42¼″.

59005

59008

59009
This fine mahogany mirror reflects the mature Chippendale style. The original was made in Philadelphia between 1756 and 1762, and may be seen today in the George Wythe House in Williamsburg. This exact reproduction would be charming over a chest of drawers in an Early American bedroom.

Glass 12½″ x 21¾″;
overall size 18¾″ x 35¼″.

59132
Serenely beautiful, the antique American looking glass which inspired this graceful adaptation hangs today in the Raleigh Tavern in Williamsburg. The mahogany adaptation has the soft curves of the original Chippendale piece made between 1750 and 1775. Beveled glass optional.

Glass 15½″ x 27¼″;
overall size 21½″ x 40¾″.

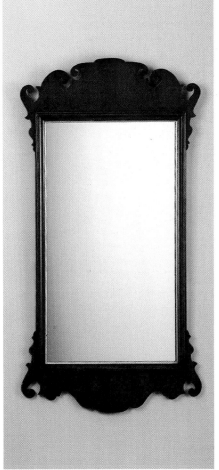

59009

59132

Two 39304 chairs and a 38039 tea table enhance this comfortable setting. Over the mantel are Catesby Prints 14007 Bahama Pintail and 14008 Buffle Head Duck.

FRENCHMAN'S MAP

This is an exact copy of a map of Williamsburg as it appeared about 1782, drawn by a French cartographer after the battle of Yorktown. The original map has been of tremendous value to the architects and archaeologists of Colonial Williamsburg in verifying the location of numerous eighteenth-century sites.

58111 Unframed, 29½″ x 22½″ including margins.

14111 Framed in black and gold molding, 29½″ x 24″.

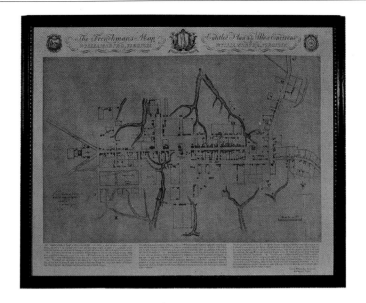

HISTORIC AMERICAN MAPS

These attractive and historically important maps are exact facsimiles of the originals.

NEW ENGLAND 1780
58608 Unframed 14⅛″ x 17⅝″.

NORTH AMERICA 1650
58610 Unframed 13⅛″ x 18⅝″.

NEW FRANCE 1719
58611 Unframed 15¼″ x 18⅜″.

New England 1780

North America 1650

New France 1719

THE WESTERN HEMISPHERE 1626
58609 Unframed 14¼″ x 18½″.

THE WORLD 1635
58607 Unframed 13½″ x 18″.

The Western Hemisphere 1626

The World 1635

YORKTOWN, VIRGINIA IN 1781
58606 Unframed 23⅛″ x 17⅜″ including
margins.

FRENCH AND AMERICAN
ENCAMPMENTS
IN WILLIAMSBURG, 1781
58603 Unframed 23″ x 17¾″ including
margins.

COLONIAL AMERICA, 1718
58605 Unframed 22½″ x 17⅜″ including
margins.

VIRGINIA, MARYLAND AND
DELAWARE IN 1755
58604 Unframed 22½″ x 17⅜″ including
margins.

Yorktown, Virginia in 1781

Williamsburg, 1781

Colonial America, 1718

Virginia, Maryland and Delaware in 1755

BODLEIAN PLATE

This is a copy of a print from a copper-plate of about 1740, preserved by the Bodleian Library, Oxford, and given by them to Mr. John D. Rockefeller, Jr. It shows the then existing public buildings of Williamsburg and native Virginia flora and fauna. It provided important evidence for the restoration of Williamsburg.

58104 Unframed, 17¼″ x 13¾″.

14104 Framed in black and gold, 18½″ x 15″.

MAPS OF EARLY VIRGINIA

These three detailed maps are similar to the 200-year-old originals now in the Williamsburg collection.

NOVA VIRGINIA TABULAR
58601 Unframed, 24¼″ x 19⅛″.

VIRGINIAE ET FLORIDAE
58602 Unframed, 22⅞″ x 19⅛″.

MAP OF VIRGINIA
58106 Unframed, 18″ x 15¾″.

14106 Framed in black and gold, 19¼″ x 17″.

Map of Virginia

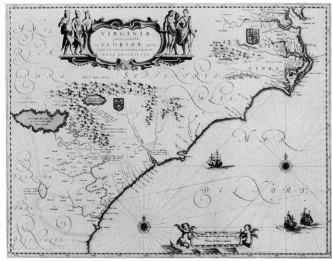

Nova Virginia Tabular

Virginiae et Floridae

HAND-TINTED PRINTS
BY THE DIETZ PRESS
Fine reproductions of Robert Furber's floral and fruit prints, and Mark Catesby's prints have been made available through the Dietz Press. Modern connoisseurs will appreciate the detail and care taken in reproducing these famous eighteenth-century prints. Each one has been reproduced on the highest quality rag paper, then hand-tinted by artists who have duplicated the original rich colors. In their day, they were used in sales catalogs and reference books, and soon became collectors' items. Today these reproductions are in great demand as decorative accessories. A wall with an entire set is an impressive sight, but a single print or a pair stand well alone.

	Framed	Unframed
The Golden Wing'd Woodpecker	14013	58013
The American Partridge	14002	58002
The Painted Finch	14005	58005
The Partridge	14001	58001
The Chatterer	14006	58006
White Bill'd Woodpecker	14012	58012
The Blew Grosbeake	14004	58004
The Red Crested Woodpecker	14016	58016
The Crested Jay	14011	58011
The Red Bird	14003	58003
The Fox Coloured Thrush	14014	58014

The Golden Wing'd Woodpecker

The American Partridge

The Painted Finch

The Partridge

The Chatterer

White Bill'd Woodpecker

The Blew Grosbeake

The Red Crested Woodpecker

The Crested Jay

The Red Bird

The Fox Coloured Thrush

CATESBY PRINTS

Mark Catesby, distinguished English naturalist, traveled to the New World in 1712, and again in 1722, to study and observe the flora and fauna of Virginia and the Carolinas. For four years he painted the birds and flowers of the new land. Of his work he wrote, "In designing the Plants, I always did them while fresh and just gathered: and the Animals, particularly the Birds, I painted while alive . . . and gave them their gestures peculiar to every kind of Birds, and where it could be admitted, I have adapted the Birds to those Plants on which they fed; or have any relation to."

Unframed, 18½" x 24" (including margins).

Framed in black with gold-leaf trim 18" x 23".

	Framed	Unframed
The Little Owl	14009	58009
Pork and Schoolmaster Fish	14015	58015
Buffle Head Duck	14008	58008
Brown and Black Tail Fish	14017	58017
Croaker and Squirrel Fish	14010	58010
Bahama Pintail	14007	58007

The Little Owl

Pork and Schoolmaster Fish

Buffle Head Duck

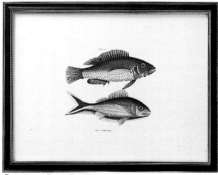
Brown and Black Tail Fish

Croaker and Squirrel Fish

Bahama Pintail

ROWLANDSON PRINTS

Not only did daily life in the country differ markedly from that in town, these delightful cartoons show that there was a significant difference at 4 A.M., too. The originals were designed and etched by Thomas Rowlandson in 1788. Colored in muted tones of blue, yellow, and beige, the reproductions are amusing and attractive decorations.

Unframed, 19" x 16" including margins.

Framed in black and gold molding, 18½" x 15¼".

	Framed	Unframed
Four O'Clock in the Country	14103	58103
Four O'Clock in Town	14102	58102

Four O'Clock in the Country

Four O'Clock in Town

FRUIT PRINTS

Robert Furber, the same English nurseryman who in 1730 had published "Twelve Months of Flowers," in 1732 issued a series of plates called "Twelve Months of Fruits." The twelve prints illustrate 364 varieties of fruit grouped according to the months in which they ripen. Accurately and brilliantly "coloured to the life," they were unlike anything else ever published in England and were in such demand in their day that they were soon impossible to obtain. Twelve mint-condition originals are in the Colonial Williamsburg collection.

A different fruit print is available for each month of the year. Please specify month desired.

Unframed, 18½" x 24" (including margins).

Framed in fruitwood with gold-leaf trim. 20½" x 26½".

	Framed	Unframed
January	14401	58401
February	14402	58402
March	14403	58403
April	14404	58404
May	14405	58405
June	14406	58406
July	14407	58407
August	14408	58408
September	14409	58409
October	14410	58410
November	14411	58411
December	14412	58412

January

February

March

April

May

June

July

August

September

October

November

December

FLORAL PRINTS

In 1730 Robert Furber, an English nurseryman, published an unusual flower catalogue. On each of its twelve pages he illustrated graceful arrangements of flowers grouped according to the month in which they bloom. Four hundred varieties, all of which could be purchased in London nurseries, were accurately illustrated and identified. Intended primarily as a sales catalogue, the "Twelve Months of Flowers" was an immediate artistic success and as such has been treasured for more than two hundred years.

A different flower print is available for each month of the year. Please specify month desired.

Unframed, 18½" x 24" (including margins).

Framed in black with gold-leaf trim. 18" x 23".

	Framed	Unframed
January	14801	58801
February	14802	58802
March	14803	58803
April	14804	58804
May	14805	58805
June	14806	58806
July	14807	58807
August	14808	58808
September	14809	58809
October	14810	58810
November	14811	58811
December	14812	58812

January

February

March

April

May

June

July

August

September

October

November

December

179

JOHN ABBOTT PRINTS 58137

The originals of these prints were painted in watercolor by John Abbott in Georgia, circa 1790. John Abbott was born in London in 1751 and immigrated to Virginia in 1773. At the beginning of the Revolution he moved to Georgia. Very much like Mark Catesby, Abbott is known to have drawn the natural life that he observed during his travels. Sold as a pair only, matted. Blue Jay and Summer Red Bird.

Each print 13¼″ x 16¼″.

58137

LIMITED EDITION PRINTS BY JOHN A. RUTHVEN

John A. Ruthven has earned international recognition as an artist who paints wildlife with anatomical exactness and attention to infinite detail. Ruthven's paintings possess a living quality that few wildlife artists have been able to capture. He has painted this series exclusively for Colonial Williamsburg. Available unframed only, 16″ x 20″.

Bob White Quail 58127
Blue Jays 58126
Mockingbirds 58128

Bob White Quail

Blue Jays

Mockingbirds

NASTURTIUM HERB PRINT
STRAWBERRY HERB PRINT

Tucked behind picket fences and criss crossed by neat brick paths, Williamsburg's charming little herb gardens beckon the visitor to see and smell a variety of the plants that were cultivated in colonial America for their medicinal and flavoring values. Each of the prints shown here illustrates nine of these useful species, drawn in the tradition of eighteenth-century botanical prints to capture the delicate details of blossom, stem, and foliage. Each plant's common and botanical name appears in the legend. Handsomely line-embossed in the manner of the old stone printing method, these colorful prints are double matted and framed in a fruitwood molding.

17½″ x 20½″.

Also available unframed, 18″ x 22½″.

14131 Nasturtium Herb Print, framed
14132 Strawberry Herb Print, framed
58131 Nasturtium Herb Print, unframed
58132 Strawberry Herb Print, unframed

Nasturtium Herb Print

Strawberry Herb Print

WATERCOLOR PRINTS BY KENNETH HARRIS

The well-known Virginia artist, Kenneth Harris, painted the originals from which these fine prints were taken. Mr. Harris is a member of the American Watercolor Society, and has exhibited his work in more than 50 museums and galleries from New York to Texas. The pleasing colors and meticulous detail of these delightful scenes make them treasured mementoes of a Williamsburg visit.

ALONG DUKE OF GLOUCESTER STREET
58118 Unframed, 34⅜″ x 24¼″ including margins.

14118 Framed in mahogany and gold leaf, 35″ x 25¼″.

WREN BUILDING
58116 Unframed, 25¾″ x 18⅞″ including margins.

14116 Framed in mahogany and gold leaf, 28″ x 21″.

BRUTON PARISH CHURCH
58117 Unframed, 25¾″ x 18⅞″ including margins.

14117 Framed in mahogany and gold leaf, 28″ x 21″.

14118

14116

14117

MERSKY PRINTS

An exclusive edition of signed and numbered etchings by the well-known American artist, Leonard H. Mersky. Only 300 were struck from each original copperplate approved by Colonial Williamsburg for this first edition. Available unframed with mat (13″ x 12″) or framed in gold (15½″ x 14⅝″).

	Framed	Unframed
Duke of Gloucester Street	14714	58714
Bruton Parish Church	14715	58715
The Capitol	14722	58722
Raleigh Tavern, South West View	14726	58726
The Capitol, South West View	14727	58727
Carter's Grove	14728	58728
The Governor's Palace	14721	58721
The Wren Building	14723	58723

Duke of Gloucester Street

Bruton Parish Church

The Capitol

Raleigh Tavern, South West View

The Capitol, South West View

Carter's Grove

The Governor's Palace

The Wren Building

WATERCOLORS BY TERRENCE COFFMAN:

The originals of this lovely series of four watercolor tavern scene prints were painted by Terrence Coffman. These prints capture the ephemeral beauty of the four seasons as experienced in Williamsburg. Each scene is in a limited edition of 1,250 signed and numbered prints.

Unframed 18″ x 24″. Framed and matted 20″ x 25½″ in 1″ antique gold metal leaf frame.

	Framed	Unframed
Chowning's Tavern-Fall	14135	58135
Wetherburn's Tavern-Winter	14136	58136
Raleigh Tavern-Spring	14133	58133
King's Arms Tavern-Summer	14134	58134

Chowning's Tavern-Fall

Wetherburn's Tavern-Winter

Raleigh Tavern-Spring

King's Arm Tavern-Summer

LIGHTING FIXTURE REPRODUCTIONS

The soft glow of candlelight, once a necessity for the eighteenth-century homeowner, is used today to create a feeling of warmth, leisure and gracious relaxation. You will find, in this collection, chandeliers, sconces and lanterns which may be used today much as they were two hundred years ago. Each of these reproductions is a careful copy of a lighting fixture used in the restored buildings of Colonial Williamsburg, and in each case the character of the original has been faithfully preserved by the master craftsmen of Virginia Metalcrafters.

Available for use with candles, all fixtures have also been adapted to electricity.

Illustrated below is 28008 Capitol Chandelier.

RALEIGH TAVERN CHANDELIER
Polished or antique brass, or polished or antique pewter. Available with four lights (like the original), five lights, or six lights.

Height 18½″; diameter 23″; total length 37″ w/2 suspension links.

		Candles	Electrified
4 arms	Brass	28116	28016
4 arms	Pewter	28119	—
5 arms	Brass	28117	28017
6 arms	Brass	28118	28018

28017

GOVERNOR'S PALACE CHANDELIER
Your choice of polished or antique pewter. Available with four lights (like the original), five lights or eight lights.

Height 20″; width 28¾″. Total length 40″ with 20″ of suspension chain.

	Candles	Electrified
4 arms	28111	28011
5 arms	28112	28012
8 arms	28113	28013

28013

APOTHECARY SHOP CHANDELIER
Polished or antique brass. Available with six lights (like the original) or five lights.

Height 18″; width 19″; total length 38″ with 20″ of suspension chain.

	Candles	Electrified
5 arms	28114	28014
6 arms	28115	28015

28115

185

GOVERNOR'S OFFICE CHANDELIER

Polished or antique brass, with eight arms. Two indirect lights inside base.

Height 40″; width 32″; total length 52″ with one foot of suspension chain.

28120 Candles
28020 Electrified

28020

CAPITOL CHANDELIER

This brass chandelier is a fine reproduction of the kind that brought light and cheer to colonial houses since the early years of the eighteenth century. The original one was probably first made in Holland about 1710.

Height 24″; diameter 26″; total length 40″ with 16″ suspension chain, brass (polished or antique) 12 arms.

28108 Candles
28008 Electrified

28108

TIN CHANDELIER

This sophisticated, six-arm chandelier was copied from an American antique of the late 1700's. The graceful spareness of the design could add a charming touch of Williamsburg to a contemporary dining room.

Height 27″; width 24″; height with canopy and suspension chain 41½″.

Antique tin or painted black.

28107 Candles
28007 Electrified

28007

PRINTING OFFICE CHANDELIER

Antique tin or tin painted black. Available with four lights; five lights or six lights (like the original).

Height 15″; width 26½″; total length 45″ with four suspension links.

	Candles	Electrified
4 arms	28104	28004
5 arms	28105	28005
6 arms	28106	28006

28005

RALEIGH TAVERN BAR CHANDELIER

Antique tin or tin painted black. Available with four lights, five lights, six lights, or eight lights (like the original).

Height 11½″; width 27″; total length 39½″ with four suspension links.

	Candles	Electrified
4 arms	28100	28000
5 arms	28101	28001
6 arms	28102	28002
8 arms	28103	28003

28003

187

CAMPBELL'S TAVERN
CHANDELIER 28009

This handsome two-tiered lighting fixture has been copied from one of a pair of wood and iron chandeliers now hanging in Christiana Campbell's Tavern. The originals were made in New England about 1785.

Height 26"; width 30"; total length 38" (suspension chain 12").

28109 Candles
28009 Electrified

28009

CAMPBELL'S TAVERN
CHANDELIER, SMALL 28010

A one-tiered adaptation of the 28009 chandelier.

Height 18"; width 23"; total length 37½" (suspension chain 20").

28110 Candles
28010 Electrified

28010

GAOLER'S LANTERN

Lanterns of this type were popular in the eighteenth century. They are now available in two styles, with softly gleaming antique tin finish.

HAND LANTERN 28310
5½" x 5½"; height 16". One light, candle (illustrated right).

WALL LANTERN 28204
5½" x 5½"; height 14". One light, electrified (for indoor use).

28310

188

BRUSH-EVERARD LANTERN
Polished or antique brass.

Height 23″; width 10½″; total length 39″ with 16″ of suspension chain. Available with four lights or one light.

28300 1 light Candle
28200 4 lights Electrified

BRUSH-EVERARD LANTERN SMALL 28201
Polished or antique brass.

Height 18″; width 8″; total length 32″ with 16″ of suspension chain. Three lights, electrified.

HALL LANTERN
Polished or antique brass, with beveled glass panels.

Height 12½″; width 9¼″; total length 44″ with 12″ of suspension chain.

28308 1 light Candle
28208 4 lights Electrified

WATCHMAN'S LANTERN
Antique tin or antique brass.

Height 21″; width 9″; total length 35″ with 14″ of suspension chain. Two lights, electrified.

28309 2 lights Candle
28209 2 lights Electrified

GOVERNORS'S PALACE LANTERN
Polished or antique brass.

Height 34″; width across corners 18″; total length 46″ with 12″ of suspension chain. Six lights electrified.

28306 1 light Candle
28206 6 lights Electrified

GOVERNOR'S PALACE LANTERN, SMALL
Polished or antique brass.

Height 18″; width across corners 11″; total length 38″ with 20″ of suspension chain.

28207 four lights, electrified.

TAYLOE HOUSE LANTERN
Polished brass or verdigris brass, with three lights.

Height 23″; width 10″; total length 39″ with 16″ of suspension chain.

28302 1 light Candle
28202 3 lights Electrified

WYTHE HOUSE LANTERN
Polished or antiqued brass, with three electrified lights.

Height 23″; width 12″; total length 39″ with 16″ of suspension chain.

28305 1 light Candle
28205 3 lights Electrified

CAMPBELL'S TAVERN LANTERN
An unusual six-sided lantern of antiqued wood and tin, copied from a New England antique of the late eighteenth century.

Height 14½″; width across corners 7¾″; height including canopy and suspension chain 28½″.

28303 Candle
28203 Electrified

28200

28208

28209

28206

28205

28202

28203

PALACE WARMING ROOM SCONCE
Polished or antique brass.

Backplate height 10½″; backplate width 4⅛″; arm projects 10⅝″. Electrified or unwired for candles.

28500 Candles
28400 Electrified

HOUSE OF BURGESSES SCONCE
Polished brass.

Backplate height 6¼″; backplate width 3¼″; arms project 7″. Electrified or unwired for candles. Mounted on walnut backplate when electrified.

28506 Candles
28406 Electrified

28500

28406

DOUBLE-ARM SCONCE 28505
Polished or antique brass with handmade crystal globes.

Total height with globes 17″; total width 15½″; backplate diameter 3⁵⁄₁₆″ arms project 9″. Available only for candles.

28505

BRUTON HURRICANE SCONCE
Polished brass with handmade crystal globe.

Total height with 10″ globe, 17″; with 13″ globe, 20″; backplate diameter 3¾″; arm projects 12″. Electrified or unwired for candles.

	Candle	Electrified
10″ globe	28504	28404
13″ globe	28503	28403

DOUBLE-ARM BRUTON HURRICANE SCONCE
This adaptation has the same design and measurements as single arm sconce, but with double arms. Available with 10″ globe only. Electrified or unwired for candles.

28502* Candles
28402* Electrified

*Adaptation

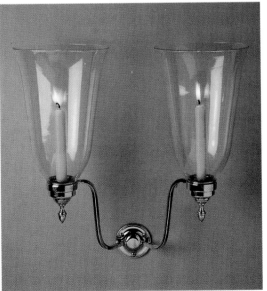

28504

28502

SERVANTS' QUARTERS SCONCE
Antique tin.

Height 10″; width 4½″; projects 4¾″.
Candle or Electrified.

28515 Candle
28415 Electrified

**WYTHE HOUSE KITCHEN
SCONCE 28513**
Antique tin.

Backplate height 8½″; width 2½″;
projects 2¾″. Candle only.

**PALACE CRIMPED-EDGE
SCONCE 28509**
Antique tin.

Height 13½″; diameter 11½″; projects
5¼″. Candle only.

**PALACE SAUCERBACK SCONCE
28511**
Antique tin.

Height 10⅜″; diameter 9⅜″; projects
5½″. Candle only.

PALACE KITCHEN SCONCE 28507
Antique tin.

Height 12″; diameter 10″; projects 4½″.
Candle only.

PRINTING OFFICE SCONCE 28517
This tin sconce is copied from an
antique of the period 1780 to 1820.

Height 13″; width: 3⅞″ bottom, 5⅛″
top; projects 6″. Candle only.

**WEST CARRIAGE GATE
LANTERN 28213**
Polished copper or copper finished
black.

Height 22½″; width 11″; projects 9½″.
Two lights, electrified.

GUARDHOUSE LANTERN 28212
Polished copper, or copper finished
black.

Height 17⅜″; width 14¾″; projects
10½″. Two lights, electrified.

**EAST CARRIAGE GATE LANTERN
28210**
Polished copper or copper finished
black.

Height 17¾″; width 11⅜″; projects 7″.
Two lights, electrified.

**EAST CARRIAGE GATE LANTERN,
SMALL 28211**
Size adaptation of 28210 East Carriage
Gate Lantern.

Height 13″; width 6¾″; projects 4½″.
Not shown. Two lights, electrified.

Left to right: 28515, 28513, 28509, 28511, 28507, 28517

Left to right: 28213, 28212, 28210

191

WILLIAMSBURG LAMPS

This group of adaptation lamps will lend the perfect touch to both traditional and contemporary settings. All are based on antiques in the Colonial Williamsburg collection.

17TH-CENTURY CANDLESTICK LAMP 22674

A massive, polished brass candlestick makes a magnificent lamp. Stunning on an executive's desk at home or in the office. Your choice of black or white shade.

Height 20½"

22674 black shade

22682 white shade

BRUSH-EVERARD CANDLESTICK LAMP 22676

The bold curves, and flaring trumpet base of a seventeenth-century English antique candlestick were the inspiration for this lamp. It is available with either a white or black shade.

Height 21½"

22676 black shade

22681 white shade

CANDLESTICK LAMP 22675

Of probable French origin, the reproduction displays the graceful lines of the original candlestick. With its adaptation into a lamp the lines of the stick create a handsome lamp. Available with a white or black shade.

Height 21½"

22675 black shade

22683 white shade

TALL CANDLESTICK LAMP 22634

More than two feet tall, this will add drama to any setting. It is a careful copy of a Continental antique now in the Capitol. Available as two-light lamp, with white silk shade.

Height 27½"

22674

22676

22675

22634

192

OCTAGONAL PEWTER CANDLESTICK LAMP 31033

A stately pewter candlestick copied from an antique in the Brush-Everard House.

Shade: Stretched off-white silk.

Height 26¾"

QUEEN ANNE CANDLESTICK LAMP 31034

The unusual faceted base distinguishes this handsome lamp, meticulously copied by Stieff's craftsmen from a pair of rare Queen Anne candlesticks. The originals made in London about 1715 can be seen in the Brush-Everard House.

Height 21½".

TOBACCO JAR LAMP 24077

A Dutch delft tobacco jar of the late eighteenth century has been adapted as a lamp to command attention wherever it might be placed.
Shade: Off-white silk piped in blue.

Height 27½"

BLUE DELFT VASE LAMP 24080

An English antique of about 1700 was copied to create this charming lamp. Three painted scenes make it attractive from any angle.

Shade: Hand-sewn off-white silk.

Height 27¾"

31033

31034

24077

24080

193

A warm and inviting family room with shelves filled with books and *Williamsburg* decorative items.

DECORATIVE ITEMS
BRASS AND WOODEN ACCESSORIES, FIRETOOLS, AND LOCKS

Mementos of the past can be as useful as they are decorative. A wide range of articles were fashioned of wood and metal by craftsmen well versed in the properties of their raw materials. Working painstakingly with the best stock he could obtain, the eighteenth-century craftsman blended beautiful design with practicality. He knew the importance of proportion and balance, and learned to achieve them without sacrificing durability. Many excellent examples of these artisans' work have survived to become prototypes for an important part of Colonial Williamsburg's Reproductions Program.

Eighteenth-century brass was whiter and brighter than most of the modern metal. Colonial Williamsburg's reproductions are made of solid brass, formulated to duplicate the color of the best eighteenth-century metal. The same techniques and tools that a colonial foundry would have employed are used today by the gifted craftsmen of Virginia Metalcrafters, Inc., Waynesboro, Virginia. Candlesticks in a variety of designs are

seen in the exhibition rooms in Williamsburg's Historic Area. They are faithfully reproduced and finished so as to be resistant to tarnish. Particularly distinctive are the elegant Urn and "S" door knockers to grace a principal entrance.

The doors of many Williamsburg homes and public buildings were equipped with large rim locks and hinges made of fine brass. Installed toward the interior of a room so that their polished surfaces and clean lines accented the symmetry of a paneled door, these handsome fixtures provided both security and ornamentation.

Today, Colonial Williamsburg's reproduction hardware is made by the Folger Adam Company of Joliet, Illinois, in a variety of sizes to fit modern doors. In order to attain the highest degree of fidelity, brass from an original lock was analyzed and the resultant formula duplicated in casting these modern replicas. Each lock case is then hand filed and polished and the works carefully fitted. Brass hinges, in examples that range from the bold H and HL designs to the delicate dovetail style, are also carefully copied from antiques found in Williamsburg.

Many articles of wood used in eighteenth-century Williamsburg become attractive accessories in the modern home. It's interesting to note that small wooden objects often reflected the current furniture style and were crafted with the same skill and attention to detail found in the finest furniture pieces. Shaving mirrors, tea caddies, wine servers, and butler's trays were all small-scaled examples of the cabinetmaker's art. Copied meticulously by local craftsmen of Victorius, Inc., Waynesboro, Virginia, these wooden items are as fashionable and functional today as their antique counterparts were two hundred years ago.

The fireplace, more a source of warmth than light, occupied a focal position in the rooms of eighteenth-century Williamsburg, upstairs and down, and was suitably provided with accessories.

The beauty and design of fire tools such as tongs, shovel, and poker, andirons, and fenders were very handsome during this period. Original examples of these durable objects are to be seen in restored Colonial Williamsburg homes. As reproductions by the Harvin Company

of Waynesboro, Virginia, they form attractive (and still useful) additions to today's fireplace. The brass finials of andirons were brought to a high polish to reflect fire and candlelight. And the foot often suggested the style of the period—a Chippendale ball-and-claw, a Queen Anne slipper, or a William and Mary ball foot. The cast-iron firebacks, solid and utilitarian guards to protect the back of the fireplace and to reflect the heat, were often decorative and unusual pieces of eighteenth-century equipment. Whether plain back with simple lines or a highly embellished coat of arms, these pieces add charm to a glowing fire.

Even the most essential equipment of eighteenth-century households reflected great attention to style and beauty. These important accessories cast the light and warmth of the colonial period into our own rooms and hallways. Their ageless design is indeed contemporary.

Brass articles are cast from a special white "antique" brass formula, and the castings are trimmed, ground, and polished by hand with special compounds to produce a pleasing and lasting finish. Bobeches can be removed for cleaning, and note the small hole in the cup of a candlestick for easy removal of candle stubs. Feature an indestructible shoe horn and gently curving jamb hook. The electrification of some of the sconces and chandeliers is concealed by casting small copper tubes within

the arms of the fixture. Reproductions, like antiques, are cast in sand and retain the small pits and polished blemishes characteristic of fine brass.

Notice the look and feel of a polished rim lock cast from special brass and the resounding clack from working parts that have been cut, hand-filled, and fitted to work smoothly.

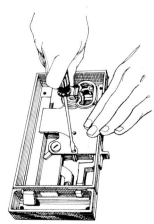

Williamsburg ®

BRASS CANDLESTICKS AND
ACCESSORIES BY
VIRGINIA METALCRAFTERS
The graceful designs of antiques in the
Williamsburg collection have been
carefully duplicated by master craftsmen, proud of their skill and the
beautiful pieces they produce. Ancient
techniques are used, and the eighteenth-
century metal, whiter and brighter in
color than modern brass, has been
painstakingly reproduced. In addition,
a special lacquer finish is applied to
each piece. This closes the pores of the
metal so that it resists tarnish, and
gives it a distinctive mellow patina.

TALL CANDLESTICK 22234
More than a foot tall, this will add
drama to any setting. It is a careful
copy of a Continental antique now in
the Capitol. The reproduction is also
available as a two-light lamp, with
white silk shade.

22234. Height 12½".
22634. Lamp height 27½".

Left to right: 22634, 22234

CANDELABRA 22263
A serpent's head decorates each branch
of this elegant reproduction, and it has
arms that move up or down and
swivel to give an entwined effect.

Height 16".

22263

SPIKED CANDLESTICK 22233

Massive and magnificent, this candlestick with wrought-iron spike was
copied from a seventeenth-century
English antique. It is dramatic alone
or with the 60100 Hurricane Shade
(page 225). A white candle is included.
For other candles please see page 202.

Height 7½″, exclusive of spike.

22233

OCTAGONAL BASE
CANDLESTICK 22235

The original of this eighteenth-century
candlestick, of Dutch origin, is now in
the Governor's Palace. It fits neatly
under the 60090 Hurricane Shade
(page 225), and is charming in pairs on
a small mantel.

Height 7″.

22235

ROUND BASE CANDLESTICK
22202
The classic lines of this serenely lovely candlestick add charm to any room. Use it alone, in pairs, or with the 60100 Hurricane Shade (page 225).

Height 8″

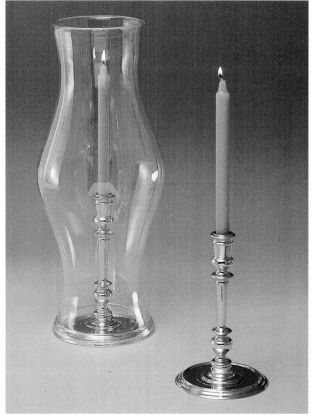

22202

BALUSTER CANDLESTICK 22220
Perfect proportions and purity of line distinguish this simple candlestick. It was copied from an early eighteenth century English antique now in the Raleigh Tavern. Use it alone, or with the 60090 Hurricane Shade (page 225).

Height 5¾″.

22220

TAPERSTICK 22239

This miniature brass candlestick holds a tiny taper, and the original was made in England in the late 1600's to melt the wax used to seal documents and letters. It can be used for the same purpose today, or simply as a pretty accessory on desk, coffee table, or by the bedside. Use it alone, or with the 60080 Hurricane Shade (page 225).

Height 4".

16110 Hand-Dipped Beeswax Candles are available for use in 22239 taperstick. See page 202.

Height 6¾".

SQUARE BASE
CANDLESTICK 22205

The original of this fine reproduction may be seen in one of the committee rooms of the colonial Capitol. A Queen Anne design of about 1720, it is square based with ridged ball feet.

Height 6¾".

22239

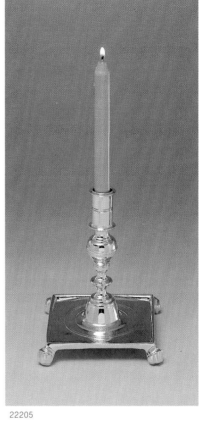

22205

CANDLEHOLDER WITH
SNUFFER 22273

This delightful reproduction has been copied from an old English piece now at Carter's Grove. It is perfect with colonial furnishings, charming in a contemporary room.

Diameter 6".

TRUMPET BASE
CANDLESTICK 22224

Contemporary in spirit, this fine reproduction is a replica of an early eighteenth century English design.

Height 8¼".

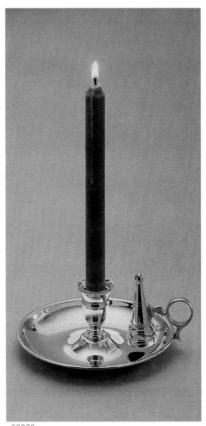

22273

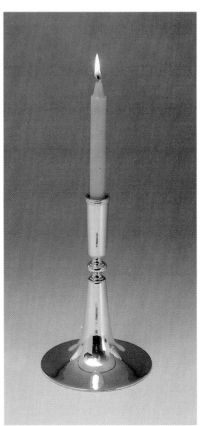

22224

SWIRL BASE CANDLESTICK 22210
The special detail of this striking candlestick has been copied from an English antique made about 1750.

Height 8¾".

MID-DRIP CANDLESTICK 22212
The drip-pan on this handsome candlestick is not only graceful but practical. It has been reproduced from an antique, circa 1680.

Height 8½".

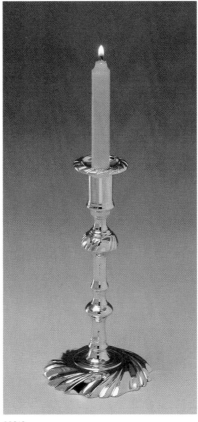

22210

22212

CANDLESTICK 22236
A handsome antique, probably French origin, has been copied to make this fine brass candlestick. The reproduction faithfully matches the graceful lines of the original, which may be seen in the Governor's Palace.

Height 9".

BRUSH-EVERARD CANDLESTICK 22213
A seventeenth-century English candlestick now in the parlor of the Brush-Everard House was the model for this handsome reproduction. Its bold curves, sausage turning and flaring trumpet base are lovely and distinctive.

Height 8".

22236

22213

200

CANDLEHOLDER 22238

This enchanting little candleholder, with a simple six-star design on the handle was copied from an eighteenth-century piece. It may be hung on a wall, or used on a side table.

Height 6½".

22238

CHAMBERSTICK 22221

The original of this graceful chamberstick was made in the mid-eighteenth century and is now in the Raleigh Tavern. It adds a bit of old-fashioned charm where ever it is placed.

Length, including handle 8½"; height 2½".

22221

TRAVELING CANDLEHOLDERS 22237

To be assured of light, the eighteenth-century traveler frequently carried his candlesticks with him. Modeled after an original made about 1770, the candleholder is compact when not in use. When opened, it becomes two graceful small candleholders.

Diameter 3¾"; height 2½".

22237

CANDLE EXTINGUISHER 22227

Conical devices of this type were known as extinguishers in the eighteenth century. Snuffers were of scissors form. This reproduction, with its free-swinging brass cone and long burnished steel handle, is especially well suited for extinguishing candles surrounded by hurricane shades. Also handy for putting out tall tapers.

Length 12".

SCISSORS CANDLE SNUFFER 22218

This delightful Williamsburg reproduction was copied from an English candle snuffer, made circa 1720-1735. Also used as a wick trimmer.

Length 6¼".

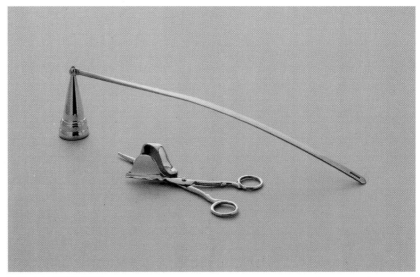

Left to right: 22227, 22218

WILLIAMSBURG CANDLES

Medium Candles (9¼")
16004 Bayberry
16107 Beeswax

Tall Candles (12")
16412 Honey (beeswax/paraffin)
16512 White (paraffin/stearic acid)
16612 Red (paraffin/stearic acid)

Spiked Candles (8½" to fit 22233 Spiked Candlestick)
16005 Bayberry
16305 Green (bayberry/paraffin)
16408 Honey (beeswax/paraffin)
16209 White (paraffin/stearic acid)
16608 Red (paraffin/stearic acid)
16108 Beeswax

Tapers (6¾" tall to fit 22239 and 31047 Tapersticks)
16410 Honey (beeswax/paraffin)
16510 White (paraffin/stearic acid)
16610 Red (paraffin/stearic acid)
16110 Beeswax

"S" DOOR KNOCKER 22668

This classic, distinctive design enhances any door, of traditional or contemporary design. This knocker is also used on many doors in Colonial Williamsburg.

7¾" x 2¾".

URN DOOR KNOCKER 22667

These fine reproductions are used on a number of Colonial Williamsburg's restored houses. The plain bar area is an appropriate place to engrave your name.

7¾" x 4¼".

22667

22668

The vital art of coopering is demonstrated in the Taliaferro-Cole Shop.

Williamsburg®

WOODEN ACCESSORIES

In today's world of production line assembly, it is unusual to find beautiful objects, carefully made by hand. Each wooden accessory in the Reproductions Program is handmade by skilled craftsmen. Copied in exquisite detail from eighteenth-century antiques belonging to Colonial Williamsburg, these fine accessories are meticulously cut, assembled, and finished by hand in the old tradition of superb craftsmanship.

OBLONG TEA CADDY 35102

This handsome caddy can hold cigarettes or cards, and it is also available velvet lined and fitted as a jewel box. It has three compartments with removable partitions. The original was made in England about 1760, and was veneered. The adaptation is solid mahogany.

Height 6″; length 10″; depth 6″.

35103 Jewel Box.

CHIPPENDALE MIRROR 35104

Scrolled and curved in the distinctive Chippendale manner, the mahogany frame of this fine mirror was copied in detail from the original, hand-cut in about 1770.

Overall height 19½″; width 9½″.

WALL BRACKET 35109

A fine copy of an antique made about 1760, this mahogany bracket is excellent for displaying a small clock, a candlestick, or a small floral arrangement.

Height 9″; width 12½″; depth 8″.

SPOON RACK 35131

A mahogany adaptation of a late eighteenth-century antique, this spoon rack has two horizontal racks with slots for twelve spoons. Illustrated with six 31056 pewter spoons (page 240).

Height 23″; width 12½″; depth 5⅜″.

Left to right: 35104, 35109

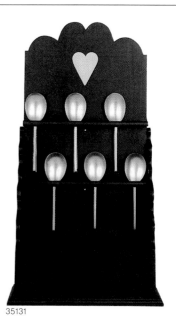

35131

OCTAGONAL TEA CADDY 35101

This mahogany container has more than 25 hand-assembled parts. Complete with foil lining and polished brass hardware, it is copied from an English piece made about 1760 and can hold jewelry, cards, or tobacco.

Height 4¾″; diameter 6¼″.

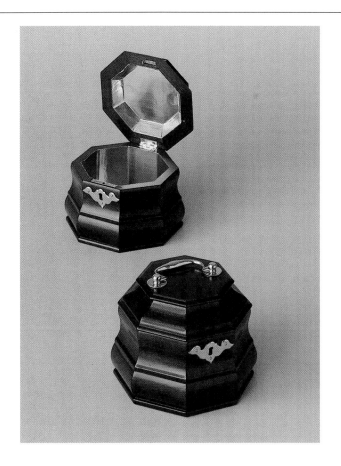

WINE SERVER 35126

A very special conceit for the man who thought he had everything! This wine server not only cradles the wine at the proper angle, but also catches any drops that might fall. It is a reproduction of an antique.

Height 4⁵⁄₁₆″; length 13¼″; width 4½″.

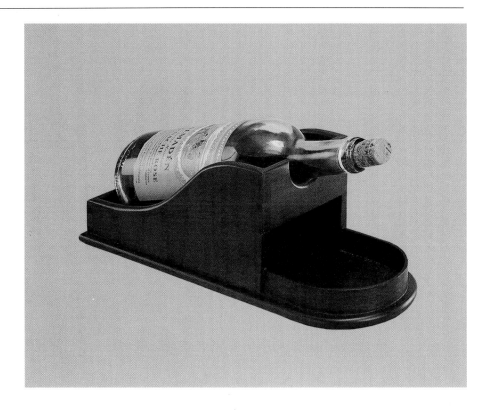

HURRICANE CANDLEHOLDER
35180

The pedestal of this unusual candle-holder is made of mahogany and supports a 10-inch, mouth-blown hurricane globe. It is a handsome accessory for any table, indoors or on porch or patio.

Overall height 16¼″.

CANDLESTAND 35129

The exquisite turnings, solid base and tray top of this mahogany candlestand are copied from an English antique of about 1770. Useful as well as ornamental, candlestands were often placed on side tables to raise candlesticks to greater height. (Shown here with the 31087 Pewter Chamberstick.) Today they often hold flower arrangements or trailing plants.

Height 8½″; diameter of top 6″.

35180

35129

WOODEN WALL LANTERN 35181

This pleasing mahogany wall lantern, reproduced from an English example of about 1775, will be an attractive addition to any room. Shown here with a 22237 traveling candleholder (page 201).

Height 16⅛″; width 6⅞″; depth 6⅞″. Inside shelf 4¾″ x 4¾″.

WALL SCONCE 35130

The gleam of candlelight is reflected from the mirrored back of this unusual dark mahogany sconce, copied from an antique in the Peyton Randolph House. The curved glass front slides up for easy access to the candlestick. Shown here with the 22220 Baluster Candlestick (page 198).

Height 18″; width 13⅝″; depth 6½″. Inside shelf depth 4½″.

35181

35130

QUEEN ANNE TRAY 35125

The simple grace of this mahogany tray with hand-carved corners and square bracket feet is reminiscent of silver trays of the Queen Anne period. Reproduced with a heat and alcohol resistant finish, it becomes a welcome asset at coffee, tea or cocktail time. Shown at left with a pewter teapot, creamer and sugar bowl (31080, 31081 and 31082). The antique may be seen in the Brush-Everard House.

Height 1¼″; length 18³/₁₆″; width 13″.

GAMING BOARD 35127

The parquet squares of this handsome board are made of rich contrasting woods, meticulously fitted. A fitting complement to your finest chess or checker set. The two 31055 tankards and 31064 pipe rest add a convivial note. It is copied from an antique now in the Wythe House. 17¼″ square.

GALLERY SERVING TRAY 35120

This unusual mahogany tray, copied from an antique now used in the Governor's Palace, has a pierced and mitered rim with carved hand holes. Alcohol and heat resistant, it serves as an excellent cocktail or tea tray. Two trays make handsome "in and out" baskets on an executive's desk. It neatly holds two 60060 decanters. 9½″ x 16½″.

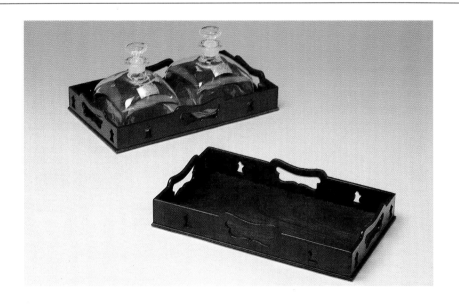

FIREPLACE ACCESSORIES
BY THE HARVIN COMPANY
Through the ages, man has used fire
for his comfort and delight. The pleasures of the fireplace make it a natural
focal point in any room, a source of
light and heat and unequalled charm.
The handsome accessories shown in
this collection of Williamsburg treasures will enhance the beauty of your
own fireplace, and dramatize this
important area of your home.

A merry fire shows to advantage in this
setting with 23111 Charles Rex Fireback, 22101 Claw-and-Ball Andirons,
22131 Firetools supported by 22800
Jamb Hooks and 22121 Serpentine
Fireplace Fender.

CLAW–AND–BALL ANDIRONS
22101

These handsome reproductions were copied from a pair of brass andirons made in the late eighteenth century, and now used in the Wythe House student's room.

Height 24″; depth 22½″.

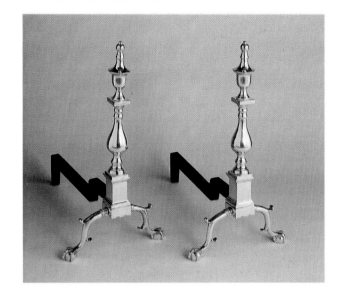

DAVIS ANDIRONS 22104

The ball-and-steeple finials on these reproductions are unusually graceful. The brass andirons were copied from a pair of antiques in the Williamsburg collection. The antiques are marked "J. Davis, Boston," and were made between 1803-1823.

Height 17″; depth 15½″.

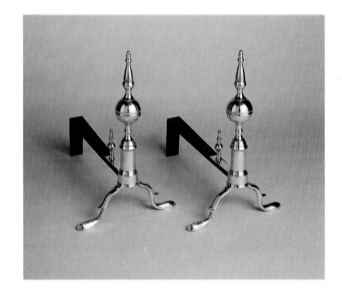

RALEIGH TAVERN
ANDIRONS 22102

Boldly designed with large brass steeple tops, these brass andirons were copied from a pair of American antiques. The originals were made in the late eighteenth century, possibly in New York or Pennsylvania.

Height 23½″; depth 22″.

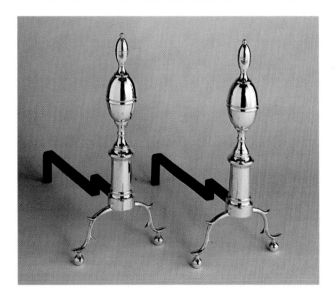

FIRETOOLS 22134

These graceful brass and polished steel tools were copied from an antique set made in England in the first quarter of the nineteenth century. Like the originals, which are now in the Moody House, they have ball finials. They are also available with finials to match the 22101 Claw-and-Ball Andirons, the 22102 Raleigh Tavern Andirons, and the 22104 Davis Andirons.

Average height 29″.

*22134 Raleigh Tavern Finials
*22133 Claw-and-Ball Finials
*22132 Davis Finials
*22131 Ball Finials

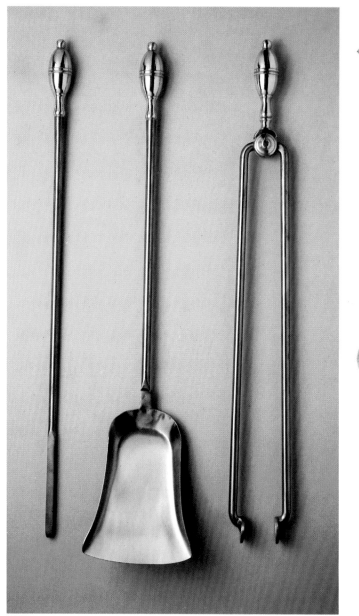

22134

22133

22132

22131

JAMB HOOKS 22800

The polished brass "chimney hooks" from which these are reproduced support fire tools on either side of the fireplace in the Brush-Everard House. Used singly or in pairs, each comes with four brass screws for mounting.

Backplate length 2⅞″; width 1⅛″; hook projects 3¾″.

BRASS HOOK 22608

Copied from an English antique of about 1785, this brass hook has many uses from a tieback for draperies to a chimney hook.

Over-all length 4⅜″.

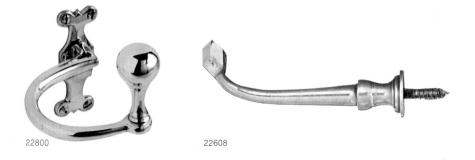

22800

22608

*Adaptation

CHARLES REX FIREBACK 23111
The royal arms of King Charles I of England embellish this elaborate cast-iron fireback. The reproduction was copied from an antique made in England in the second quarter of the seventeenth century, now used in the Governor's Palace.

Height 23″; width 21″.

VIRGINIA FIREBACK 23112
The legend "Virg^a 1737" decorates the face of this cast-iron fireback. The reproduction was copied from antique fragments excavated at the site of the Red Lion on Duke of Gloucester Street in Williamsburg.

Height 24″; width 20¾″.

PANEL FIREBACK 23113
This cast-iron fireback was copied from an antique used in the Governor's Palace. Fragments of a duplicate fireback were excavated at the site of the Palace; experts believe the two might have come from the same foundry and mold. The antique was made in the first half of the eighteenth century.

Height 24″; width 18½″.

IRON KETTLE 23611
This authentic hearth accessory adds a nostalgic touch to any fireplace, or makes an unusual planter for porch or patio. It has slightly concave sides and rounded bottom, copied from an old English piece in the Williamsburg collection.

Height 6⅜″; diameter 6½″

23111

23112

23113

23611

Firebacks may be used as unusual decorative pieces, and their original use, to reflect heat and protect the back wall of the fireplace, is still valid.

SERPENTINE
FIREPLACE FENDER 22121
A simple pierced pattern with a scalloped edge distinguishes this handsome brass fender. It was copied from an English antique circa 1790 and now in the office of the Peyton Randolph House.

Height 6¾″; width 49¼″; depth 11⅝″.

Williamsburg ®

BRASS HINGES AND RIM LOCKS BY FOLGER ADAM

Careful attention to detail is the distinguishing mark of a beautiful home. These reproductions are careful copies of locks and hinges used in eighteenth century Williamsburg, now seen again in Williamsburg's restored houses and exhibition buildings. This handsome hardware, carefully crafted by Folger Adam in the classically simple style, will be a tribute to your good taste.

KEY

KEY ESCUTCHEON AND FLAP
WITH CYLINDER LOCK
Optional with the Brass Rim Locks #1 and #2 only.

DROP HANDLE AND ROSE
Optional with the Brass Rim Lock

KNOB
Solid brass, optional to use with interior or exterior locks.

The Williamsburg Rim Lock, so called because the entire lock is exposed, is made of heavy brass, hand-fitted and polished by expert craftsmen. It is available with solid brass knobs or drop handles. It includes a complete lock assembly with one large brass or stainless-steel key. For those who do not wish to carry a large colonial key, the #1 and #2 locks are also made with a covered key escutcheon, and with a modern cylinder lock unobtrusively fitted to the large lock, and operated by a small key. Knob or drop handle sets for use with modern mortise latches are also available.

The locks are made in three different sizes to fit the scale of individual doors with right-hand or left-hand openings. The side of the door on which the keeper is placed determines whether the lock is right or left hand. Orders should specify lock size, whether right or left hand, the thickness of door, and preference for either brass or stainless steel key. See price list.

#1 Large. 10" x 5¾" x 1⅜"
#2 Medium, 8" x 4½" x 1"
#3 Small 6¾" x 4" x ⅞"

Keeper   57202 Left-hand medium lock with drop handle.

These handsome polished brass HL and H hinges are reproductions of antiques found in Tazewell Hall, a Williamsburg house built about 1725. The original of the 56600 is in the Peyton Randolph House. Available in different sizes and combinations to accommodate any door.

	Length	Overall Width
56611HL	11¾"	14⅞"
56621HL	8¾"	11¼"
56610H	11¾"	4½"
56620H	8¾"	3⅝"
56600	4¼"	4½"

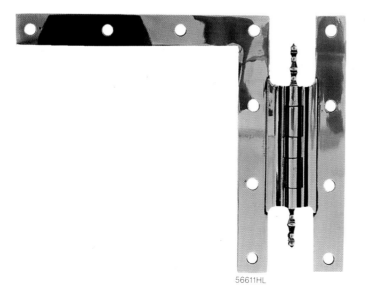
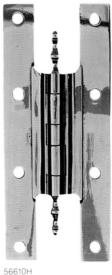
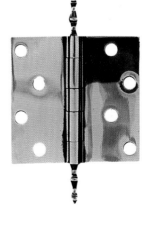

56611HL   56610H   56600

The entrance hall of the Governor's Palace. Reproduction firearms and swords may be seen
page 264.

DINNERWARE, CRYSTAL, SILVER AND PEWTER

In Colonial Virginia, hospitality was unstinted. Records show that people visited friends or relatives for weeks—not infrequently for months. After all, travel time itself could occupy days or weeks. Travelers armed with proper letters of introduction could expect to stay with perfect strangers for prolonged periods of time.

Private hospitality was supplemented by that of colonial taverns and inns—where one could find accommodations for himself and his horse, meet friends, dine, talk politics, complain about and even agitate against the royal government. Not least of all, inns and taverns were places to carouse. Parties to welcome incoming officials, for example, might extend far into the night.

Despite some boisterousness of manners, hospitality of the day demanded the setting of a fine table in homes or taverns. In every aspect of dining and hospitality the colonists demonstrated an appreciation of the arts in their choice of silver, pewter, glass, and in their pottery and china. The products of these same arts are available today in the careful reproductions and adaptations made for Colonial Williamsburg. Because of the Reproductions Program, many value-conscious Americans are setting a gracious table, mixing and matching the eighteenth and twentieth centuries as their tastes and habits dictate.

DINNERWARE
From its earliest days, Williamsburg imported ceramic wares from England as a necessity of life. Dinnerwares ranged from a common pottery called delftware (made in England at the time, in spite of its Dutch name) to the sophisticated products of Josiah Wedgwood, who founded his factory at Burslem, in Staffordshire, in 1759. The Wedgwood saga became a success story following the invention of the famous "cream ware," later called Queen's Ware to honor Queen Charlotte, wife of George III. She patronized Wedgwood and named him "Potter to Her Majesty."

Bone china was developed in English potteries during the last few years of the eighteenth century, and by the beginning of the nineteenth century this refined translucent porcelainware had gained the popularity it still retains. The Wedgwood Company has today produced for Colonial Williamsburg dinner services of the same fine bone china, including reproductions of early Wedgwood pieces in the Colonial Williamsburg collection and in the Wedgwood Company's own museum.

As in the earlier days, these beautiful pieces set their own standards of excellence in table fashions for the modern home. Williamsburg's decor for dinnertime establishes the pattern for a good table of the twentieth century.

GLASSWARE
Treasured and well-guarded glasswares of two hundred years ago are in the Colonial Williamsburg collections. Many comparable fragments have been recovered from archaeological excavations. From these fragments came, for example, the pattern for the now famous baluster glass reproductions.

Traditional and distinctive dinnerware shapes for use in both period and contemporary settings: wide rim dinner plates with steep shoulders, tea cups with deep saucers, carving forks with guards, and large knives of fine Sheffield steel.

The luster of 32% lead crystal—like the antique—more difficult to work than ordinary glass, but more durable. Mouth-blown and hand-formed, 18th- and early 19th-century shapes reproduced down to a teardrop or airtwist within stems of vases, goblets, and wine glasses. Look for a small bubble or stone, inherent both to antique and fine reproduction glassware.

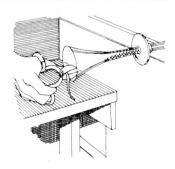

The first glassmakers in America were "eight Dutchmen and Poles," who landed at Jamestown, Virginia, in 1608. They used techniques of glassmaking developed many centuries ago. Similar techniques are used today by the artisans at Royal Leerdam, one of the few glass manufacturers continuing the delicate art of off-hand glass-blowing. Williamsburg glassware is made of lead glass, a strong translucent material with a high capacity for light diffusion. The stemware adds classic distinction to modern table settings with goblets, wine glasses, and champagne/sherbet glasses in patterns of airtwist, teardrop, and baluster. These are contributions of the glassblowers' art. Additionally, reproductions or adaptations of colonial decanters in graceful and sophisticated shapes serve to furnish bar or side table in a fashionable decor.

In the eighteenth century hurricane shades were used to protect candles from drafts. Hurricane shades especially used in combination with silver, brass, or glass candlesticks form a particularly pleasing accessory for hallway table, side table or dining table and are available in three sizes.

SILVER AND PEWTER
Even people of modest means in colonial Virginia owned sterling silver, imported in large part from England, but also fabricated locally. Williamsburg counted some fifteen men who in one way or another dealt in silver in the seventy-year period before the Revolution. There were silversmiths and goldsmiths, jewelers, engravers, and watch-makers. Like James Geddy, Jr., the most famous of their number, all imported wares from England and advertised them for sale in the *Virginia Gazette.* The gentry bought silverware as a form of investment as well as a symbol of status, and their silver possessions are recorded in inventories. Theirs was the age of "Georgian," the greatest period in the history of domestic silver.

Pewter, an alloy of ancient origin (composed of tin, copper and antimony), was widely used in the American colonies for articles of domestic use.

Both silver and pewter pieces have come down intact from the eighteenth century. Many originals command extravagant prices as prized and sought-after articles of both rarity and beauty. From such museum treasures, the Kirk-Stieff Company of Baltimore has made superb reproductions in silver and pewter. The pewterware is cast, turned, burnished, and polished to produce lustrous bowls, spoons, plates, sugar casters, and inkwells. The silverwares, produced by casting, spinning, and hammering, and meticulously brought to a high polish,

include full tea and coffee services, sugar bowls, spare bowls, and creamers; table accessories such as sauce boats, salt cellars, pepper and mustard pots, sugar casters, and candlesticks. Available as reproductions are the Queen Anne and Shell patterns of sterling flatware. These were popular throughout much of the eighteenth century and today their traditional and handsome designs of knives, forks, and spoons are highly distinctive.

Plated silverware follows an English traditional method of plating silver. Several items of silverplate are available as adaptations of eighteenth-century antiques.

Silverware, solid or plated, is timeless and brings to our dining table the same richness, the same quality it lent to the good tables of our colonial forebearers.

Hand-chased sterling silver. Carved ebony handles on coffee and teapots. Weight and characteristics of antique silver.

Pewter free from impurity of lead and highly polished to a luster typical of fine antique pewter.

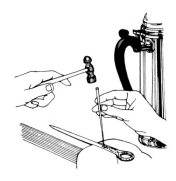

59014 mirror, 39065/66 dining table, Cuckoo china, Airtwist crystal and Williamsburg Shell flatware at home in the 20th century.

BONE CHINA BY WEDGWOOD

Bone china was developed in the English potteries during the last few years of the eighteenth century, and by the beginning of the next, it had become the standard ware of the fine English porcelain factories. So high was the quality of the English bone china that it continued to be the porcelain produced throughout the nineteenth century and—with only minor improvements—is still used today.

For a decade during the first quarter of the nineteenth century the Wedgwood company, managed by Josiah Wedgwood II, son of the great Josiah Wedgwood who, more than fifty years earlier, had founded the factory, produced this refined, translucent ware. It was decorated with many and varied patterns; some incorporating new motifs designed specifically for the ware and others taken from successful old patterns extending well back into the eighteenth century.

The Wedgwood firm has today produced for Colonial Williamsburg dinner services of the same fine bone china, including reproductions of early Wedgwood pieces in the collections of Colonial Williamsburg and in the Wedgwood company's own museum. To conform with twentieth-century table customs some pieces have become altered in size or form, and when no example from the period could be found to copy, as in the coffeepot, compatible forms were designed.

The decoration of the Wedgwood bone china services produced for Colonial Williamsburg include patterns used on Wedgwood's original bone china employing both motifs designed for the ware and patterns dating back to the period of the first Josiah, as well as a familiar bone china pattern produced by neighboring factories during the same period.

CHINESE TIGER

This dog-of-foo design, or Chinese tiger as it was called in the early nineteenth-century, is found on pieces of a tea service in the Wedgwood museum and on a plate owned by Colonial Williamsburg. Examples in other museums appear in colors, such as red, blue, and black.

CHINESE FLOWERS
The interest in things Oriental can be seen in these, an early nineteenth-century Englishman's conception of "Chinese flowers." They are so described in Wedgwood's pattern book.

BIANCA
Probably the most familiar early nineteenth-century bone china pattern is this basket of flowers, used by several potteries but primarily by Wedgwood's Staffordshire neighbor, New Hall. There the pattern was employed on both earthenware and hardpaste porcelain before it was produced on bone china. Two other recorded New Hall patterns have been employed by Wedgwood, in conjunction with the basket of flowers, to unify the designs.

CUCKOO
This colorful chinoiserie pattern is reproduced from the motifs found on a coffee cup and saucer in Colonial Williamburg's collection. It also appears in Wedgwood's pattern book where it is referred to as "flowers and bird."

Williamsburg ®

QUEEN'S WARE
BY WEDGWOOD

Queen's Ware was an invention of Josiah Wedgwood, a skilled and successful potter, who said in 1767, "The demand for this . . . Queen's Ware . . . still increases. It is really amazing how rapidly the use of it has spread almost over the whole globe, and how universally it is liked." Originally called cream ware by its inventor, it was soon to bear the name Queen's Ware at the command of Queen Charlotte of England, whose admiration for Wedgwood's work was further expressed when she made him "Potter to Her Majesty."

The tradition of excellence established by Josiah Wedgwood is carried on by his descendants, who work today with the same high standards of design, skill, and integrity he set two hundred years ago.

WILLIAMSBURG IRIS

This commemorative pleasingly adapts the copperplate fabric reproduction "Williamsburg Iris" into Wedgwood's Queen's Shape dinnerware. Available in the full range of place setting sizes. The fabric may be seen on page 151.

POTPOURRI

Named for Queen Charlotte, Wedgwood's Queen's Shape dinnerware has been made continuously since 1765. In this delightful commemorative, it is imaginatively decorated in a rich fruit and flower pattern taken from an antique fabric. For information about the fabric, which has been reproduced, see page 151.

Linen place mats and napkins to match, Potpourri 29720, are available.

Williamsburg Iris

Potpourri

Reflections of gracious dining with Airtwist crystal and Bianca bone china. The sterling flatware is Williamsburg Shell.

Williamsburg®

GLASSWARE
BY ROYAL LEERDAM

With their timeless simplicity of line, Williamsburg glass reproductions harmonize with contemporary as well as traditional table settings. This fine glassware is unequalled for beauty of design, purity of materials, and superb hand craftsmanship. Interpreted from fragments excavated in Williamsburg and copied from antiques in the exhibition buildings of Colonial Williamsburg, these reproductions are made of lead glass, strong yet translucent, with an extraordinary power to diffuse light. Only the finest, most experienced craftsmen are entrusted with making these mouth-blown and hand-formed pieces. Each piece has its individual characteristics, reflecting the skill of the artisan who produced it.

AIR-TWIST STEMWARE

This spiral air-twist form was developed about 1735 and was popular throughout the middle of the eighteenth century. Many fragments have been discovered in Williamsburg. In making the air-twist stemware, a wire is introduced into the molten stem to form a channel. Several channels are successively formed and then combined and twisted into a graceful spiral by the use of wooden paddles and other special tools in the hands of a master craftsman.

61033 Wine Glass. Height 6½".
61031 Goblet. Height 7⅞".
61032* Sherbet/Champagne.

Height 5¾".

Left to right: 61033, 61031, 61032

*Adaptation

TEARDROP STEMWARE

The teardrop in this intriguing pattern is formed by first introducing a wire into the molten stem. When a channel forms, a wet stick is applied and the steam develops a "tear," which the craftsman pushes up the stem to the desired spot. The teardrop sherbet or champagne glass is copied from an antique in the Williamsburg collection. Many fragments of teardrop stems were revealed in Williamsburg archaeological excavations.

61023* Wine Glass. Height 6½".
61021 Goblet. Height 7⅞".
61022 Sherbet/Champagne.

Height 5¾".

Left to right: 61023, 61021, 61022

BALUSTER STEMWARE

There is ample evidence that this was one of the favorite types of stemware in the colonial capital. Among the common stem forms found during Williamsburg excavations was this inverted baluster with sloping domed foot, an English style of the first half of the eighteenth century. The handsome reproductions of this baluster shape are still popular today because the simplicity of style complements both modern and traditional settings.

61013 Wine Glass. Height 5⅞".
61011 Goblet. Height 7⅜".
61012* Sherbet/Champagne.

Height 5".

Left to right: 61013, 61011, 61012

*Adaptation

223

PILSENER GLASS 61024*
This tall, graceful glass is excellent for serving beer or ale. Although it is an adaptation of the teardrop design, its tapered shape is in the best eighteenth-century tradition.

Height 7⅞″.

AIR TWIST WINE GLASS 61047
A set of these handcrafted lead crystal glasses would greatly enhance any formal setting. The bell-shaped bowl is supported by a particularly attractive air-twist stem.

Height 7″.

PLAIN WINE GLASS 61046*
This superbly crafted wine glass will add elegance to any table setting. The bell-shaped bowl rising from a tall, graceful stem is of a generous size, to please connoisseurs.

Height 7″.

Left to right: 61024, 61047, 61046

TALL DECANTER 60130
An antique once owned by a colonial resident of Williamsburg was copied for this handsome crystal decanter.

Capacity 1⅓ quarts; height, including stopper, 11¼″.

DECANTER 60420*
A very large decanter has been reduced in size to make this graceful adaptation. This version handles and pours with ease.

Capacity 1¼ quarts; height, including stopper, 11″.

SQUARE DECANTER 60060
This charming decanter with its wide base and low, rounded lines was copied from an antique designed to fit a cellarette. It is delightful alone or used in pairs on the 35120 Tray.

Capacity 1½ quarts; height, including stopper, 6¼″; base 6 x 6″.

*Adaptation

224

Left to right: 60130, 60420, 60060

HURRICANE SHADES

Originally used to shield candles from wind and drafts, hurricane shades are popular today for the same practical reason, as well as for decorative purposes. A hurricane shade may be used on its side filled with colorful fruits and nuts and pine cones, or upright surrounded by flowers, as a charming holiday decoration or centerpiece. These fine hurricane shades are size adaptations of a graceful antique in the Colonial Williamsburg collection.

60080 Hurricane Shade. A tiny shade to fit small spaces. Can be used with 22239 Brass Taperstick or 31047 pewter Taperstick. Height 9½".

60090 Hurricane Shade. Height 14"; inside diameter of base 4⅞".

60100 Hurricane Shade. Height 17¾"; inside diameter of base 5⅝".

Left to right: 60100, 60080, 60090

BALUSTER CANDLESTICKS 60450

An English antique (circa 1720), now in the Peyton Randolph House, inspired these fine crystal pieces. The simple rounded lines of the baluster design are just as appealing now in any table setting.

Height 8½".

TEARDROP CANDLESTICKS 60110

An exquisite pair of candlesticks reflecting the skill of modern craftsmen working by hand in the eighteenth-century manner. Eight separate pieces of glass are carefully joined to form the shaft of each candlestick where a "teardrop" resides. Particularly lovely on a dinner table or mantel.

Height 8¹⁄₁₆".

Left to right: 60450, 60110

225

PLAIN FLIP GLASS 60150
This simple, handsome glass makes a stunning tall vase. Its shape is copied from an English antique.

Height 7½".

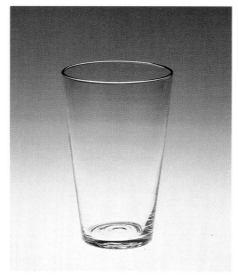

60150

HIGHBALL GLASS 60430
Any table or bar would be enlivened by these handsome glasses, the perfect size and shape for today's entertaining.

Height 5½"; capacity 12 ounces.

OLD FASHIONED GLASS 60320*
A size adaptation of the 60310 Double Old Fashioned Glass, this is especially popular for cocktail parties because of its compact size.

Height 3¼".

DOUBLE OLD FASHIONED GLASS 60310
This handsome copy of an eighteenth-century tumbler is just as popular two hundred years later. The original is in the kitchen of the George Wythe House.

Height 4".

Left to right: 60320, 60430, 60310

TAVERN GLASSES
This handsome set of glasses was inspired by a fragment uncovered during excavations at Williamsburg, now in the archaeological collection. Simple, graceful, these glasses will dress up any party or table setting. 60510 is an exact reproduction; the others are size adaptations.

60530 Iced Tea. Height 6⅛".
60540 Water. Height 5⅛".
60510 Old-Fashioned. Height 4⅛".
60520 Cordial. Height 2⅞".

*Adaptation

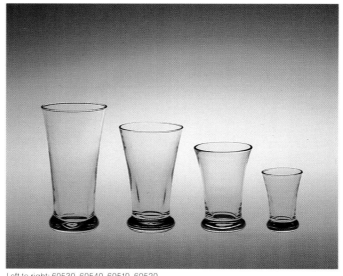

Left to right: 60530, 60540, 60510, 60520

226

WATER JUG 60380*
Simplicity is the keynote of this gently rounded pitcher, carefully reproduced and copied from a cherished antique. Etching, which decorates the original, has been omitted.

Capacity 1½ quarts; height 7⅞″.

60380

PITCHER 60360*
This pitcher is a larger size adaptation of the 60370 Pitcher.

Height 5″.

PITCHER 60370
This reproduction of a miniature eighteenth-century antique pitcher in Wetherburn's Tavern can be used as a small creamer or a vase for tiny flower arrangements.

Height 3⅝″.

Left to right: 60360, 60370

LIPPED FINGER BOWL 60070
Our forefathers used lipped bowls to rinse their wine glass between wine courses. Today these dainty bowls serve as finger bowls, and for ice, dessert, nuts, or flowers. The reproduction was copied from an antique in the Williamsburg collection.

Height 4¼″; diameter at top 4½″.

*Adaptation

60070

227

STERLING SILVER
REPRODUCTIONS
BY KIRK-STIEFF

Williamsburg silver reproductions combine the balance, strength, and satisfying proportions of the best eighteenth-century craftsmanship. Patterned after the silver used in a gracious, hospitable society, the hollow ware and flatware shown on the following pages have the direct simplicity and superb design characteristic of that elegant age. These handsome copies of colonial antiques, equally suitable in traditional and contemporary settings, increase in beauty with each day's use.

Even persons of modest means in colonial Virginia are known to have owned sterling silver. For the wealthy, sterling silver was a form of investment as well as a symbol of status and a necessary and appropriate part of table service. The graceful pistol-handled knives, three-tined forks, and rat-tailed spoons, and the handsome coffeepots, bowls, and pitchers now reproduced and available at Craft House are as satisfying to own today as they were two hundred years ago.

COFFEEPOT 32229
The original of this magnificent coffeepot was made by Charles Le Roux, a New York silversmith. The straight spout and straight tapered sides contrast dramatically with the curves of its ebony side handle.

Capacity one quart; height 11″.

32229

TEAPOT 32219
The melon-shaped body of the Williamsburg teapot is balanced by the sweeping curve of its ebony handle. Delicate hand engraving around the top is its only ornament. The antique it copies was made by Boston silversmith, Jacob Hurd.

Capacity 1½ pints; height 6″.

32219

SUGAR BOWL 32215
Simple yet elegant, this bowl was copied from one made 200 years ago by John Burt, a Boston silversmith.

Capacity 10 ounces; height 2¾″; diameter 4″.

SUGAR BOWL COVER 32216
The unusual shape of this smoothly rounded cover is both practical and charming. It has its own foot and may be used separately as a small dish. It fits the 32215 Sugar Bowl.

Height 1¼″; diameter 4¼″.

Left to right: 32215, 32216

228

SUCKET FORK 32072

A reproduction silver sucket fork, originally intended for syrupy desserts that required both fork and spoon, today is practical for cocktail olives or onions.

Length, 6¾".

32072

BRANDY WARMER 32267

An old English saucepan, made by John Eckford in 1723, inspired this graceful reproduction. An excellent way to serve melted butter or hot sauces.

Capacity 8 ounces; height 2¼"; length, including handle, 6¾".

32267

SAUCE OR GRAVY BOAT 32222

The jaunty sweep of its curved handle balances the long, graceful lip of this fine reproduction. The original was made in Boston by John Burt.

Capacity 10 ounces; overall length 8".

32222

CREAMER 32218

This is a size adaptation of a creamer thought to have been made by John Allen (1671-1760). Its shape echoes the soft curves of the 32215 Sugar Bowl.

Capacity 10 ounces; height 4½".

BOWL 32228

A design of classic simplicity copied from a bowl made by Philip Syng (1676-1739). This fine reproduction serves beautifully as a waste bowl for the Williamsburg tea or coffee service, or as a candy dish.

Capacity 18 ounces; height 2⅝". diameter 5½".

32228

32218

TRENCHER SALT 32231

An antique made in London circa 1706-1707 was copied in this graceful open salt dish, glass-lined to guard the silver from corrosion.

Height 1¼"; diameter of base 2⅜".

CUP 32271

Simple lines and a graceful handle distinguish this silver cup copied from an American example of about 1795. It is perfect for serving punch and equally serviceable as a baby's cup.

Height 2⅞".

32231

32271

REPRODUCTION FLATWARE

SHELL PATTERN

This Shell Pattern sterling silver service is based on an assembled set of English, Georgian flatware in the Colonial Williamsburg collection. It dates from about 1760. The raised shell on each piece is characteristic of the period, and is found on many English produced items during the middle years of the eighteenth century. Various forms, unknown in colonial times, have been adapted from the antique pieces. And note, the fork has four tines rather than three.

32401	Dinner Knife
*32402	Luncheon Knife
†32404	Service Spoon
32405	Tablespoon
*†32407	Bread and Butter Knife
32408	Coffee Spoon
†32409	Dinner Fork
†32410	Luncheon Fork
*32411	Cocktail Fork
*†32412	Teaspoon
*32413	Iced-Tea Spoon
*32414	Roast Carving Set
*32454	Salt Spoon
*32460	Cold Meat Fork
*32461.	Steak Knife
*32463	Gravy Ladle
*32464	Fish Knife
*32468	Baby Spoon
*32469	Baby Fork
*32470	Sugar Shell

Left to right: 32410, 32411, 32409, 32407, 32401, 32404, 32413, 32408, 32454, 32405, 32412,

QUEEN ANNE PATTERN

The Williamsburg Queen Anne sterling silver pattern has been recognized for years as a most distinguished reproduction of eighteenth-century flatware. Copied from a design popular throughout most of the eighteenth century, the rat-tailed spoons, three-tined forks and pistol-handled knives are cherished today as then for their graceful shapes and clean lines.

32601	Dinner Knife
32602	Medium Knife
*†32603	Small Dinner Knife
†32604	Dessert Spoon
32605	Tablespoon
32606	Tablespoon (notched)
*†32607	Butter Spreader
32608	Coffee Spoon
†32609	Dinner Fork
†32610	Medium Fork
*32611	Oyster Fork
*†32612	Teaspoon
*32613	Iced-Tea Spoon
*32614	Roast Carving Set
32651	Ladle
*32654	Salt Spoon
*32660	Cold Meat Fork
*32661	Steak Knife
*32662	Steak Carving Set
*32663	Gravy Ladle
*32664	Fish Knife
*32665	Salad Fork
*32668	Baby Spoon
*32669	Baby Fork
*32670	Sugar Shell

Left to right: 32665, 32609, 32610, 32603, 32602, 32607, 32604, 32613, 32612, 32605, 32606

†Six Piece Place Setting
*Adaptation

CANDLESTICK 32224
Silversmith Timothy Bontecou (1693-1784), made the original of this classic candlestick, which harmonizes so well with any setting. The oval of its removable cup reflects the shape of the base.

Height 5½″.

DECANTER LABELS 32006
Boxed set of six sterling silver decanter labels or specify your choice of bourbon, scotch, gin, vodka, rye, rum, brandy, sherry or port. The individual label may be seen on page 265.

32006

32224

PEPPER SHAKER 32236
A perfect partner for the 32231 Trencher Salt, this handsome caster can also be used as a muffineer for nutmeg or cinnamon. The antique was made in Boston by Benjamin Burt (1729-1805).

Height 5¼″.

SET OF SIX STEAK KNIVES 32699
QUEEN ANNE PATTERN
See page 231.

PLATED SILVERWARE

Plated silverware has had its place in the finest homes since about 1742, when an English cutler first discovered that silver and a base metal could be fused and worked like solid silver. The Kirk-Stieff Company has produced several handsome pieces of plated silverware, copied from the original antiques, with skill and care. These pieces surpass the best grade of super-fine silver plate.

COFFEEPOT 33008*

The chaste, unadorned look of this distinguished coffeepot was copied from a sterling silver pot made in London in 1740-1741 and now in the George Wythe House.

Height 10¼"; capacity 2½ pints.

CREAMER 33005*

This dainty little creamer with its slender looped handle has softly rounded lines to match those of the 33003 Sugar Bowl.

Height 4½"; capacity 10 ounces.

SUGAR BOWL 33003*

A simple, graceful bowl made by a Boston silversmith over 200 years ago has been adapted in silver plate by Stieff craftsmen.

Height 2¾"; diameter 4".

SUGAR BOWL COVER 33004*

The unusual cover of the sugar bowl also will serve as a small footed dish for candy or nuts.

Height 1¼"; diameter 4¼".

Left to right: 33005, 33003 with 33004

SALT SHAKER & PEPPER SHAKER SET 33801

These substantial shakers were copied from a silver pepper box made by Samuel Vernon in Newport, Rhode Island about 1720.

Height 3⁵⁄₁₆".

*Adaptation

233

BOWL 33001*

This classic bowl is a silver plate adaptation of an antique now in the James Geddy House. The original was made by Richard Gurney and Thomas Cook of London. It makes a fine centerpiece or serving dish for hors d' oeuvres.

Height 3⅛″; diameter 7⅛″.

Also available in two additional sizes.
33014* Bowl 6″
33015* Bowl 9″

STANDING CUP 33009*

Copied from a Charles II silver goblet made in 1687—1688, this handsome standing cup has a nearly cylindrical bowl supported by a baluster stem and spreading circular foot. The English antique is in the Palace dining room.

Height 6″.

CUP 33011*

This silver cup with plain rim and rounded base was a type popular in Virginia in the eighteenth century. The original cup, now in the Geddy House, was made in London by John Payne in 1752-53.

Height 2½″.

COMPOTE 33006*

The beautiful and the practical combine in the simple design of this small compote, ideal for serving nuts, candies, or hors d' oeuvres.

Height 2¼″; diameter 6⅝″.

33001

Left to right: 33009, 33011

33006

CANDLESTICK 33010*

The oval socket of this well proportioned candlestick reflects the oval shape of the base.

Height 6⅞″.

CANDLESTICK 33002*

The original from which this handsome candlestick was adapted was made in London in 1723-1724 by David Green and is now in the Peyton Randolph House.

Height 6¼″; width 3¾″.

Left to right: 33010, 33002

*Adaptation

Craftsmen at work in the Geddy Foundry.

The timeless beauty of pewter is at home in any setting.

PEWTER
BY THE KIRK-STIEFF COMPANY
Pewter was one of the more widely used metals in early colonial days. Now this lustrous, durable metal is being used by the Kirk-Stieff Company of Baltimore to create a group of fine pewter pieces copied from the treasured antiques on display in Colonial Williamsburg's exhibition buildings.

PITCHER 31100
This stout pewter pitcher holds an astonishing one quart. It is copied from an antique English ale jug made about 1800. The original is now at Carter's Grove.

Height 5½".

TEAPOT 31080
An eighteenth-century antique teapot made in London by Samuel Ellis inspired this distinctive adaptation. The original, somewhat smaller teapot, is now displayed at the Raleigh Tavern.

Capacity 2¼ pints; height 8¼".

31100

31080

PITCHER 31095
A silver pitcher made by Samuel Hitchcock in London in 1728-1729 inspired this smoothly rounded pewter adaptation. It holds 90 ounces.

Height 9½".

CASTER 31099
A late eighteenth-century English antique inspired this reproduction. A caster or muffineer, it is used now as it was 200 years ago, to serve sugar and spices at the table.

Height 7".

OPEN SALT 31098
Gently rounded curves and graceful proportions distinguish this attractive open salt, a welcome accessory to any table. It is shown here with the 31090 Salt Spoon (page 240).

Diameter 2¾".

31095

Left to right: 31099, 31098

SUGAR 31082*
This softly rounded sugar bowl was designed as a charming companion piece for the 31081 Creamer.

Height 2¾″.

SUGAR 31084*
A size variation of the 31082.

Height 3½″.

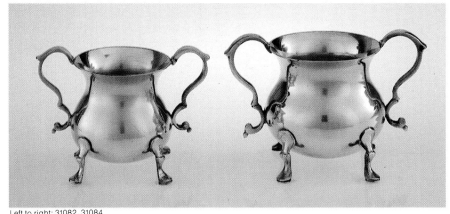
Left to right: 31082, 31084

CREAMER 31081
This graceful pear-shaped creamer is an exact reproduction of an English or American antique now in the Raleigh Tavern.

Height 3¼″.

CREAMER 31083*
A size variation of the 31081.

Height 4¼″.

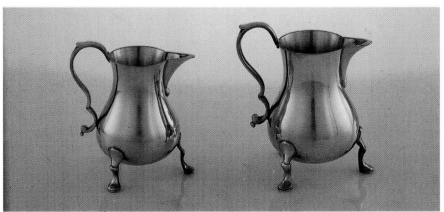
Left to right: 31081, 31083

CREAMER 31091
The fanciful, scalloped lip on this graceful creamer gives it special charm. Its antique prototype, now in the Raleigh Tavern, was probably made in England in the last half of the eighteenth century.

Over-all height 4″.

SUGAR 31092*
This gracefully rounded adaptation was patterned after the 31091 Creamer, its companion in spirit and style.

Over-all height 3¾″.

31091

31092

PORRINGER 31016
This bowl is the ideal size for serving candy, nuts, or cocktail dip. It also makes a thoughtful christening present of lasting beauty and usefulness.

Diameter 3¼″.

PORRINGER 31015
An excellent small serving dish, this handsome porringer was copied from an eighteenth-century English antique now displayed in the public dining room of the Raleigh Tavern.

Diameter 4¼″.

*Adaptation

Left to right: 31016, 31015

STRAWBERRY DISH 31054

This unique scalloped bowl, particularly suitable for fresh strawberries, is spectacular piled high with any fresh fruit. Its original was an Irish antique made circa 1690-1700 by William Bancks and now on display in the dining room of the Brush-Everard House.

Diameter 11½".

31054

PORRINGER 31060

The original of this porringer, now in the Wythe House kitchen, was made by Edward Nash of London (circa 1717-1738). This detailed reproduction makes a superb nut or candy bowl, flower container or large ash tray.

Diameter 5¼".

31060

PLACE PLATE 31059

The original of this classically simple place plate was made in London circa 1766-1777. The reproduction is excellent for serving sandwiches, cold meats and hors d' oeuvres.

Diameter 11".

PLATE 31076

This graceful small dish finds many uses in contemporary homes. It has been copied from an eighteenth-century antique.

Diameter 5¼".

Left to right: 31059, 31076

TRAY 31012*

The original from which this tray was adapted was part of a miniature pewter service, probably of Continental origin. The adaptation, is a distinctive serving tray.

Diameter 10½".

SOUP PLATE 31058

Superb as a soup plate, serving dish, large ash tray for your coffee table. It was copied from an eighteenth-century plate, now at Carters Grove Plantation.

Diameter 8¾".

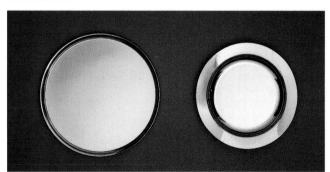

Left to right: 31012, 31058

*Adaptation

CUP 31949*
This two-ounce adaptation of the
31049 Cup is an excellent jigger for
the bar, or a charming cigarette cup for
the dining room table.

Height 2".

CUP 31049
Copied from an eighteenth-century
English beaker, this graceful cup is
equally suitable for a cocktail or a
small bouquet. It can also be used on a
coffee table to hold cigarettes, or on
a desk to hold pencils and pens.

Height 3".

Left to right: 31949, 31049

SALT SPOON 31090*
It is perfect with the 31098 Open Salt
(page 237).
Length 3".

COFFEE SPOON 31089*
Adapted from an English antique.
Length 4¼".

LADLE 31052
An authentic copy of a type of ladle
used in the late eighteenth century.
Length 5¾".

TEASPOON 31053*
A size adaptation of the 31056 Table-
spoon.
Length 6".

TABLESPOON 31056
A copy of a seventeenth-century
English antique.
Length 7".

Left to right: 31090, 31089, 31052, 31053, 31056

SUGAR SCOOP 31085
This generous scoop can be used with
the 31010 Bowl (page 242) to serve
nuts, mints or condiments. Its antique
original bore the crowned X, symbol
of English pewter of high quality.

Length 4⅞"

DRESSING SPOON 31014
This handsome heavy spoon is impressive in size and design. More than a
foot long, it makes an elegant addition
to any table service.

Length 13¼".

BERRY SPOON 31051
This unusual slim-handled spoon is an
exact copy of an English antique dating
back to the late sixteenth or early
seventeenth century.

Length 6¾".

Left to right: 31085, 31014, 31051

PEWTER CANDLE SNUFFER 31001
A delightfully different candle snuffer, this pewter pipe was copied from an antique, probably of English origin, dating from 1740-1780. Metal pipes were designed for travelers and huntsmen, for whom a clay pipe was too fragile.

Length 9¼″.
(Cannot be used as a pipe.)

31001

COPELAND SPOON 31021
The earliest known example of American-made pewter, bears the legend Joseph Copeland 1675 Chuckatuck. The original spoon handle was excavated by archaeologists working at Jamestown in 1930, and now, fifty years later, it remains the oldest piece of pewter made in America yet discovered.

Length 7¾″.

31021

BEAKER 31088
This lustrous pewter piece can be used as a drinking cup, like its original, or as a vase. It is a careful reproduction of a graceful English antique.

Height 6¾″.

CORDIAL CUP 31988*
A size adaptation of the 31088 Beaker, this smaller version makes a charming cordial cup.

Capacity 1 ounce; height 2¼″.

TANKARD 31055
Useful as well as ornamental, a handsome tankard in classic eighteenth-century design makes a gift to be treasured. Each tankard holds a pint.

Height 5″.

Left to right: 31088, 31988, 31055

SALT 31096*
& PEPPER 31097*
These matched salt and pepper shakers have been adapted from the larger 31099 Caster by Kirk-Stieff's master craftsmen. Use them as a pair to dress up your table settings. The 31097 Pepper can also be used with the 31098 Open Salt.

Height 5⅛″.

CUP 31002
This first cup for baby has an easy-to-grasp curved handle and thumb rest; it makes a charming christening gift. A Queen Anne style reproduction, it could also be used for holiday punch.

Height 2⅞″.

Left to right: 31096, 31097   31002

*Adaptation

BOWL 31009
This design of classic simplicity is copied from an antique bowl bearing English marks of the second half of the eighteenth century. It can be used alone as a serving dish or teamed with the 31005 Mahogany Basin Stand.

Diameter 10⅜″.

BOWL 31003
An excellent bowl for fruit, vegetables, or flowers, this fine reproduction is a copy of the basin made by Thomas Badger of Boston about 1800.

Diameter 8″.

31009

31003

FOOTED BOWLS
These simple, graceful, footed-bowls copied from an English antique of the eighteenth century, find many uses in the modern home. Use the smaller bowls for nuts, candy, sauces, or consomme. The larger sizes are ideal for serving fruits or vegetables; 31007 is a handsome container for flowers.

31007 diameter 11″.
31010 diameter 5½″.
31005 diameter 7¼″.
31006 diameter 9¼″.

From left to right: 31007, 31010, 31005, 31006

CANDLESTICK 31101
Eighteenth-century English pewter candlesticks with baluster-shaped stems, although quite common in brass, are extremely rare in pewter. Only a few patterns are known. This reproduction is the same weight as the original, made by George Lowes of Newcastle, England, Circa 1720.

Height 6½".

31101

TAPERSTICK 31047
This charming little candlestick, copied from one of a pair of English antiques that date from about 1690, would have been used to melt sealing wax. Today it becomes a delightful decorative accent when placed under a Hurricane Shade.

Height 3¹/₁₆".

CHAMBERSTICK 31087
In colonial days, this type of candlestick was carried up to one's bedroom. Now the reproduction makes a decorative table accessory, useful for candlelight dining, or as an ash tray or pipe rest. The original English antique is in the Williamsburg collection.

Diameter 5¾"; height 3¼".

CANDLESTICK 31030
The unusual faceted base distinguishes this handsome candlestick, meticulously copied by Kirk-Stieff's craftsmen from a pair of rare Queen Anne candlesticks. The originals made in London about 1715.

Height 7¼".

CANDLESTICK 31032
This impressive octagonal candlestick, copied from a seventeenth-century pewter antique, will reflect the glow of candlelight with warmth and elegance. Impressive when used in pairs on a sideboard or dining table.

Height 9".

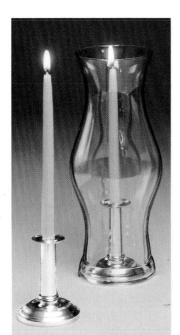

31047

31087

31030

31032

PEWTER DISH 31004
The brightly polished finish of this charming pewter dish catches the light and mirrors the graceful scallops and flutes of its design. Reproduced from an antique in the Colonial Williamsburg collection, it has a sparkle all its own.

Diameter 5″.

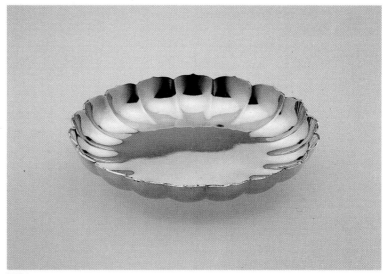

31004

PEWTER DISH 31079
This narrow rimmed reproduction pewter tray would make a lovely serving piece. The original English dish was made by Thomas King of London, about 1690 and would have been used for the service of food. The tray is quite unusual because of its narrow rim, which gives it a rather modern feeling.

Diameter 13⅞″.

CUP 31104
Simple lines and a graceful handle distinguish this pewter cup adapted from an American silver example of about 1795. It is perfect for serving punch and equally serviceable as a baby's cup.

Height 2⅞″.

31079

31104

MUG 31103*
Adapted from the 31102 tankard, the body design is identical, but the cover and thumb piece have been removed.

Height 6″.

TANKARD 31102
The original of this tankard is one of the most ambitious forms in seventeenth and eighteenth century English and American pewter. With its double-domed cover and broad body with a bold scrolling handle and well-defined moldings, the reproduction possesses the pleasing proportions and sculptural qualities prized in good pewter design.

Height 6″.

31103

31102

*Adaptation

244

SUNDIAL 31043

An eighteenth-century American craftsman made the original of this pewter piece. It is an unusual paper-weight or ornament, and can also be attached to a window ledge or garden table to serve its original purpose.

Diameter 3".

PAP BOAT 31064

The original of this unusual piece has the crowned X found on good-quality eighteenth-century English pewter. It is used here as a pipe holder, but also makes a fine ash tray.

Length 4⅜".

Top to bottom: 31043, 31064

HUMIDOR 31094

This beautifully crafted humidor is an exact copy of an English antique now used in the Apollo Room of the Raleigh Tavern. The original was made by Anthony Jenner (circa 1770-1780). This handsome Kirk-Stieff copy holds cigars, tobacco, matches.

Over-all height 7¼"; diameter of base 6".

HUMIDOR 31093*

This size adaptation of the larger 31094 Humidor makes a handsome desk accessory. Both are copied from an eighteenth-century English antique.

Over-all height 6"; diameter of base 5".

Left to right: 31094, 31093

HELMET INKSTAND 31078

The original, now in the secretary's office of the Governor's Palace, was made in England by Bush and Perkins, around 1770-1790. The reproduction, which comes complete with quill pen, adds charm to any desk.

Diameter 5".

*Adaptation

31078

The domestic craft of basketmaking is demonstrated in the Wythe House outbuildings.

WILLIAMSBURG DELFT-POTTERY-NEEDLEWORK-GIFTS

Eighteenth-century householders surrounded themselves with items of usefulness, convenience, and beauty. Two hundred and fifty years later, their counterparts, living in suburban homes or in city apartments would like to do the same. Not surprisingly, some articles then in common use have now become exceedingly rare. Many cups, bowls, jars, and jugs are known only by archaeological fragments which reveal the shape, pattern, and color of the originals. Such objects possess great interest and value because they record the daily life of people of another day.

Williamsburg's antique collections feature a rare assemblage of delftware, a type of decorated earthenware imported extensively into the colonies. Now recognized for their exceptional charm, color, and utility, these pieces are made by Oud Delft of Nijmegen, Holland, with such fidelity that reproductions bear the identifying date so as to avoid confusion with the antique! As jardinieres, bricks for flowers, vases, pitchers and apothecary jars, modern delftware is an attractive addition to period or modern interiors.

Williamsburg residents purchased a variety of wares from local potters to round out their household inventories. Far less sophisticated in design and execution than imported ceramics, these vessels were in everyday use, for food preparation and storage in the kitchen, or for table service in the bustling taverns and inns of the colonial capital. Produced again today by a potter in the Williamsburg area, these colorful designs and simple shapes are perfect for today's casual occasions.

Decorative ceramics were popular in the eighteenth century. The tradition is continued in the "figures"—delightful representations of Colonial Williamsburg personalities, and the character jugs of craft and tradesmen in the direct tradition of the period's Toby jugs. These exquisitely modeled and hand-painted ceramic pieces are created by Doulton and Company, a firm that dates back to 1815.

In colonial times, the art of drying flowers for use in the winter months as well advanced, as was the growing of blossoms that lent themselves to this treatment. These used to be called "everlastings" and have achieved new popularity in today's decor. Williamsburg dried flowers are prepared by 18th Century Bouquet, Incorporated, of Princeton, New Jersey, and today are used to add a splash of color to an interior in winter, as well as in summer.

Never obtrusive, always correct, these decorative items from Colonial Williamsburg add a gracious touch to today's good living.

Historic Colonial Williamsburg provides an array of attractive and unusual gifts that will delight you, your family, and your friends. Some are copies of objects once in daily use; some are reminiscent of the folk arts of the period; some evoke the atmosphere of the past in articles of our own day. These unique gifts for all ages are at once charming, evocative and educational.

Homely objects of the eighteenth century, like the trivets used as stands for hot dishes prepared in separate kitchens, have been copied in iron and brass—using elaborate and fanciful monograms, royal arms, and cyphers as themes. While they still protect a table from a steaming casserole, they are highly attractive, and usable as pure decoration for wall or table.

Mid-eighteenth-century children have left us many examples of their sampler work with the obligatory alphabet and numbers, together with artless scenes and the name and age of the busy stitcher. Sampler kits are available as gifts illustrating familiar Williamsburg scenes.

There is also a replica of little Mary Starker's elaborate sampler of 1760 for a real challenge. At a more sophisticated level, needlepoint and crewel kits reproduce early American designs from the extensive textile collections in Williamsburg. These designs can then be framed or applied to pillows and chair seats.

For the bar or sideboard, sterling silver decanter labels are reproductions of antiques; a corkscrew in brass and steel is also an authentic copy (the basic corkscrew has changed little over the centuries). Williamsburg's four famous taverns are comemorated in bright linen cocktail napkins.

Colonial Williamsburg publishes an extensive list of books and records. Besides photographic essays and titles of general appeal, there are specialized studies of the decorative arts by Williamsburg's curators, and research studies that open vistas to the past. How-to books show holiday decorations and translate eighteenth-century recipes into dishes for the twentieth-century table. Music is as much a part of today's restored Williamsburg as it was in colonial times, and high fidelity records and cassettes capture that dimension of eighteenth-century life, from the sprightly tunes played by the Fife and Drum Corps to the elegant notes of a harpsichord.

The gift giver will also find towels of fine linen, candles of beeswax and bayberry, and a potpourri of herbs, flowers, and spices ready to do duty in drawers and blanket chests. Some letter paper and notes are attractively printed with eighteenth-century motifs while others depict familiar buildings and street scenes of the colonial town. Sure to delight is that necessity for Williamsburg's favorite holiday decoration, the apple cone. Please the miniature enthusiast with an assortment of wallpaper patterns, pewter and flatware pieces, all in $1/12$ scale, for a tiny room setting or shelf display.

For a personal touch, colonial objects like a decorated keyhole escutcheon have been reproduced as an unusual pin, "the Lion and the Unicorn," while the historic symbols of authority like the Capital mace and the Williamsburg mace, are miniatured as lapel or scarf pins suitable to anchor an unusual crepe silk scarf designed from an eighteenth-century Persian carpet.

Williamsburg Gifts have been designed with the discriminating person in mind. Each one has been specially selected and carefully crafted to illustrate an authentic facet of Colonial Williamsburg. They can, indeed, provide the just-right thoughtful gift for special occasions.

A room designed for comfort. Delft tiles and candlesticks with 39666 barrel chair upholstered in Blue Coverlet Cotton.

DELFT
BY OUD DELFT OF NIJMEGEN

Delftware was a common pottery of the colonial housewife; today it is treasured in the finest homes for its grace, coloring, and style. Messrs. Oud Delft of Nijmegen, Holland have been commissioned by Craft House to copy a selection of rare delft antiques in the Colonial Williamsburg collection. So close are these copies that Colonial Williamsburg has asked the manufacturer to impress an identifying date into each piece so that none may be mistaken for an antique. The discriminating collector and decorator will find many pieces of interest in these pages.

Williamsburg Delft Reproductions, imported for Craft House by Foreign Advisory Service Corporation, are made with essentially the same techniques as were used two hundred years ago in Holland. Each piece is lightly fired before it is dipped in tin-enamel glaze, which is allowed to dry. The decoration is then applied by a skilled artist. After another firing, a final glaze is applied for brilliance, and one last firing completes the meticulous process.

CREAM JUG 24031
This adaptation was hand-painted in brilliant polychrome, inspired by a smaller jug made in Liverpool about 1760. The original is in the Raleigh Tavern public dining room.

Height 4½".

TOBACCO JAR 24060
The original of this tin-enameled earthenware piece, now on display in the Apothecary Shop, was made in the second half of the eighteenth century. Characteristic of Dutch delft, the colors are blue and white. The inscription reads, "Carolina."

Height 10⅜".

24031

24060

PITCHER 24048
Two Chinese figures, a distant town, and a delicate tree decorate this graceful pear-shaped pitcher. It is a copy of an English antique, circa 1760, now in Wetherburn's Tavern.

Overall height 9¼"; capacity 2 quarts.

PITCHER 24033
This delightful pitcher proves once again that useful objects can also be beautiful. Filled with milk or waffle batter, it will brighten the breakfast table. Multicolored flowers decorate this gay adaptation of a salt-glazed antique made about 1750-60. The original is now in the dining room of the George Wythe House.

Height 6¼"; capacity 1¼ quarts.

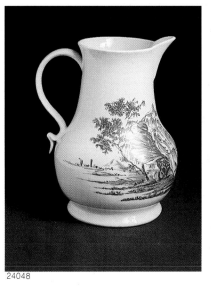

24048

24033

INKWELL 24028
A fine copy of an antique in the Williamsburg collection, this inkwell is not only a fine desk accessory, but looks delightful filled with a small nosegay. The original is a piece of Continental tin-enameled earthenware.

Height 1¾"; width 4¾".

ROUND BRICK 24040
Use it to hold your favorite flower arrangement. It is a copy of a piece of Lambeth delft, circa 1700, decorated with an abstract design.

Diameter 6".

24028

24040

OVAL DISH 24052
Painted with a design of birds, rocks and flowers, this unusual reproduction is often used as a small planter or a distinctive nut dish. The original, circa 1690, was probably used for potted meat.

Height 3¼"; length 7".

PORRINGER 24051
Copied from a Lambeth delft antique, this pleasing replica has many uses. The original was made circa 1720-30.

Height 2⅛"; overall diameter 5½".

CASTER 24053
Useful for sugar or cinnamon, or a delightful holder for bath powder, this caster is a copy of a piece of Dutch delft made in the eighteenth century.

Height 6⅜"; overall base diameter 3".

24052

Left to right: 24051, 24053

DELFT PLATE 24010
The Chinese influence is shown here in the design, in two shades of blue. Copied from an eighteenth-century English plate found at the site of the Chiswell-Bucktrout House.

Diameter 10¼".

VASE 24049
This versatile vase is decorated with three scenes of figures and landscapes. It is also available as a lamp. See page 193. Copied from an English antique, made about 1700, now in Williamsburg's Apothecary Shop.

Height 10¼"; top diameter 4½".

24010

24049

CHINESE BRICK 24026
This delightful brick is gaily decorated in soft delft colors. The original, a piece of Bristol delft, was made about 1740.

Height 2½"; length 4½".

POLYCHROME BRICK 24027
This is a reproduction of a Bristol delft piece of the mid-eighteenth century.

Height 3½"; length 6".

BLUE BRICK 24029
The Mimosa design is hand painted in the familiar delft colors on this fine replica of an English antique. The original dates from the second quarter of the eighteenth century.

Height 3½"; length 5¾".

Left to right: 24026, 24027, 24029

PUNCH BOWL 24044
The generous size of this punch bowl is enhanced by the nicely scaled design of birds, flowers and leaves in the traditional shades of blue. Fill it with punch for a festive occasion, or use it year round as a centerpiece, filled with fruit or flowers. The original was excavated in fragments from the site of the Coke-Garrett House in Williamsburg, carefully restored and now exhibited in the James Anderson house.

Height 5⅝"; diameter 10½".

MUG 24054
This bell-shaped mug is a copy of an antique made in Lambeth about 1760. A set of eight or twelve, together with the 24044 Punch Bowl make a charming and most distinctive party table.

Height 5"; capacity 12 ounces.

Left to right: 24054, 24044

JAR 24032
The original of this delicate vase was made in Liverpool in the mid-eighteenth century. In the summer months it is charming filled with sweet peas or small daisies; in the winter, with small dried flowers. The antique may be seen in the Brush-Everard House.

Height 5½".

VASE 24030
The original of this Bristol delft piece was designed between 1710 and 1720. The classic urn shape has been deftly decorated with a stylized motif.

Height 6".

24032

24030

SWEETMEAT TRAY 24055
The stylized flowers on the border, and the blue and white house in the center are typical of English delft motifs of about 1740.

Side length 4¾″.

SHELL TRAY 24047
A Chinese scene decorates this appealing shell, a copy of an antique made in Liverpool circa 1750. The original is now in Wetherburn's Tavern.

Width 3¾″.

POLYCHROME SAUCER 24041
This tiny saucer displays an intriguing hand-painted design. It was copied from an antique excavated in Williamsburg.

Diameter 4½″.

Left to right: 24055, 24047, 24041

MUG 24058*
A small adaptation of the "porter" mug, this one is just the right size for hot or cold drinks.

Height 4½″; diameter of base 3¼″; capacity 12 ounces.

"PORTER" MUG 24059
Made to quench a man-sized thirst, this delft mug was copied from an English antique which bears the name "porter," a popular beverage of the time. Today it would also serve as a vase for flowers.

Height 6″; diameter of base 4¾″; capacity one quart.

Left to right: 24058, 24059

JARDINIERE 24005
This square polychrome brick is adaptable to a variety of flower arrangements. It is a faithful copy of a Lambeth delft jardiniere, made about 1750.

Height 4″.

CANDLESTICK 24057
Unusually attractive, with hand-painted designs in varying shades of blue. It is a replica of an antique made in Liverpool (about 1750) and now in the James Geddy House.

Height 7″.

CANDLESTICK 24038*
An engaging candlestick has been adapted from the top section of a mid-eighteenth-century Lambeth delft food warmer. Like the antique, this copy has been meticulously hand painted in a crisp blue design.

Height 2½″.

24005

Left to right: 24057, 24038

252

WALLPOCKETS

Perfectly reproduced, these wallpockets are copied from antiques made in Lambeth about 1750. They were designed to be used in pairs with plants or flowers, but can be used singly for an unusual wall decoration. Alone or in pairs, they add dimensional interest to a wall gallery of pictures.

24036 Chinese Boy. Height 8″.
24037 Chinese Girl. Height 8″.

Left to right: 24036, 24037

DELFT TILE HOLDER

This trivet was adapted from the square base of an antique brass candlestick, and designed specifically to hold one of the Williamsburg delft tiles.

Iron 55010*
White-bronze 55011*

WILLIAMSBURG DELFT TILES

Cobalt blue on white, these attractive tiles are copied from those used as facing for the fireplace opening in the northeast bedroom of the Governor's Palace. They can also be used on table tops, as decorative wall ornaments, or to tile areas in kitchen, terrace or bathroom.

5¼″ square.

Tile Holder: 55011

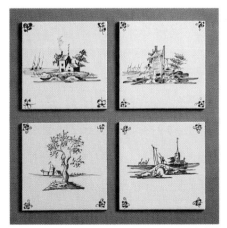

Clockwise from bottom left: 24067, 24061, 24062, 24068

Clockwise from bottom left: 24069, 24063, 24064, 24070

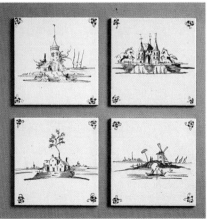

Clockwise from bottom left: 24071, 24065, 24066, 24072

*Adaptation

253

FIGURES AND CHARACTER JUGS
OF WILLIAMSBURG
BY ROYAL DOULTON

FIGURES

Doulton and Company, Incorporated, has created a group of delightful figures modeled after men and women who lived in Williamsburg two hundred years ago. These exquisite bone china figures are modeled and painted by hand by Doulton's master craftsmen. These authentic Royal Doulton figures embody the perfection, skill and artistry of years of English craftsmanship.

	Top row, left to right	
24305	Seated Lady	Height 6″
24306	Wigmaker	Height 7½″
24302	Gentleman	Height 6¼″
	Second row, left to right	
24307	Blacksmith	Height 7″
24303	Cook	Height 6″
24304	Silversmith	Height 6¼″
	Bottom row, left to right	
24309	Boy from Williamsburg	Height 5¾″
24301	Standing Hostess	Height 7½″
24308	Child	Height 5½″

CHARACTER JUGS
OF WILLIAMSBURG

These character jugs are vigorous characterizations of seven Williamsburg craftsmen of today, who wear the dress and ply the trades of their eighteenth-century predecessors. All of these commemorative jugs are hand-painted.

Available in three sizes:
Large   Height 7″
Medium   Height 4″
Miniature Height 2½″

	Large	Medium	Miniature
Apothecary	24320	24420	24520
Blacksmith	24321	24421	24521
Bootmaker	24322	24422	24522
Gaoler	24323	24423	24523
Guardsman	24324	24424	24524
Night Watchman	24325	24425	24525
Gunsmith	24326	24426	24526

Left to right: Blacksmith, Gaoler, Bootmaker, Night Watchman, Apothecary, Gunsmith, Guardsman

POSY HOLDER 24104

Reproduced from an English Staffordshire "finger vase" made about 1770, the famous Williamsburg Posy Holder is a delight to the flower lover. Fanciful arrangements can be made in it with only a few flowers.

Height 7¾".

A large box of dried flowers was used to make this arrangement in the 24104 Posy Holder.

The use of dried flowers in Williamsburg's colonial buildings has its precedent in the eighteenth century when mass bouquets of bright everlastings were widely used to harmonize with the elaborate furnishings, spacious rooms, and forthright colors of the period.

MELON DISH 24123

The cream-colored dish has been copied from an eighteenth-century mold. The covered melon-shaped bowl is fixed to a leaf tray. It is delightful for individual servings of soup and dessert, and for jellies and marmalade.

Capacity 8 ounces.

DRIED FLOWERS

Today's flower arranger will take delight in creating arrangements with the dried flowers offered at Craft House. Adaptable to both contemporary and traditional designs, the selection in each box includes a wide variety of leaves and bright blossoms such as cockscomb, strawflowers, magnolia, celosia, babies-breath, yellow yarrow, and larkspur.

The large and medium boxes are available in the following predominant colors: red, pink, gold, pastel or mixed. The small box does not include leaves and has mixed colors only about one-third the amount in the large box.

	Large	Medium	Small
Mixed	18845	18850	18851
Red	18841	18846	
Pink	18842	18847	
Gold	18844	18849	
Pastel	18843	18848	

CORNUCOPIA

Effective as wall ornaments with or without flowers, these wall pockets have been adapted in size from a pair belonging to Colonial Williamsburg. The originals are Staffordshire salt-glaze, made in England circa 1760.

Height 10".

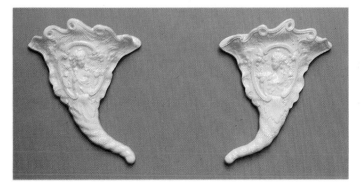

Left to right: 24922, 24122

255

POTTERY
BY WILLIAMSBURG POTTERY

Inspired by fragments excavated in Williamsburg and at Jamestown, and by antiques in the Williamsburg collection, these attractive items are handmade by local craftsmen. Using traditional incised (sgraffito) and slip-colored techniques, this stoneware is comparable to pottery used in the Williamsburg area in colonial times.

Stoneware is a hard pottery impervious to liquids and acids. This technique was invented by German potters in the fifteenth century, and adopted by eighteenth-century English potters. The techniques are used today in hand-crafting Williamsburg pottery. Many hand operations are required to make every piece.

FERN TRAY & HONEYSUCKLE TRAY

These attractive serving dishes have been copied from antique sweetmeat trays made in Staffordshire, England, about 1760. Like the originals, these reproductions are footed.

20208 Fern Tray. Length 6″.
20209 Honeysuckle Tray. Lenght 6½″.

STAR MOLD 20015

Bake individual desserts in it or use it to mold fancy gelatin salads. Every home should have several. This small star mold is an ovenproof copy of an antique mold.

Height 1½″; diameter 3½″.

FISH MOLDS

These appealing fish make excellent ash trays, pin trays, or individual hors d' oeuvres plates. The 20016 Mold is a copy of an antique; the 20017 Mold is a slightly larger adaptation. Both are ovenproof.

20016 Fish Mold. Length 5⅞″.
20017* Fish Mold. Length 8¼″.

Left to right: 20208, 20209, 20015, 20016, 20017

LARGE TRENCHER 20005

This large yellow-and-brown serving dish is copied from an antique now in the Raleigh Tavern. Ovenproof, it's an excellent choice for entertaining or large family meals. Its comb decoration is typical of eighteenth-century slipware.

Length 16¾″. Also available are two size adaptations; all are ovenproof.

20006* Small Trencher. Length 8¼″.
20014 Miniature Trencher. Length 4½″.

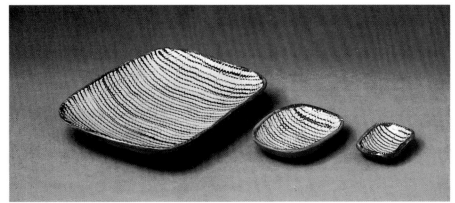

Left to right: 20005, 20006, 20014

*Adaptation

POTTERY BOWLS

These rustic slipware bowls decorated in warm tones of brown and yellow are typical of a style popular in the eighteenth century. Today they become excellent ash trays or unusual serving dishes for nuts, candy or hors d' oeuvres.

The originals are now displayed in Wetherburn's Tavern.

20036 Round Bowl. Diameter 7".
20035 Round Bowl. Diameter 7¼".
20034 Oblong Bowl. Diameter 6" x 5".

Left to right: 20036, 20035, 20034

BOWLS

A set of those yellow and brown bowls is delightful for serving individual casseroles and soups. The sgraffito or scratchware decoration is charming. Available in three sizes.

20003 Medium Bowl. Diameter 6½".
20004 Large Bowl. Diameter 7¾".
20002 Small Bowl. Diameter 4¾".

Left to right: 20003, 20004, 20002

MUGS

These gray stoneware mugs with cobalt blue decoration were inspired by fragments from the Williamsburg archaeological collection.

20011 Large Mug. Height 5¾", capacity 36 ounces.

20911 Mug. Height 4½"; capacity 16 ounces.

20012 Child's Mug. Height 3½"; capacity 7 ounces.

BEER MUG 20001

The design of this yellow and brown mug dates back to the early settlement at Jamestown, Virginia.

Height 5"; capacity 16 ounces.

Left to right: 20011, 20911, 20012, 20001

257

PRESERVE JAR 20033
A sturdy antique jar now in the Raleigh Tavern was copied to make this attractive stoneware container. Use it as a vase for leaves or flowers, or fill it with your own preserves or pickles.

Height 5⅜″.

SLIPWARE PITCHER 20007
The pleasing, rounded lines of this small pitcher were copied from early eighteenth-century fragments found on the site of the Semple House. The pitcher is yellow with streaks of brown.

Height 6″; capacity 24 ounces.

20033   20007

JUGS
Copied from antique gray stoneware jugs made in Germany for the English market. Similar ware with cobalt blue decoration is made in Germany today.

20008 Medium Jug. Height 6″; capacity 18 ounces.

20009 Large Jug. Height 8″; capacity 36 ounces.

JUG 20030
A Devonshire jug, now in the pantry of the Brush-Everard House, inspired this small slipware pitcher, done in yellow glaze with brown sgraffito decoration. Like the original, it is inscribed "E. M. 1792."

Height 5″.

PITCHER 20021
An English antique, circa 1760, inspired this charming small pitcher with its scratch blue decoration. In this kind of ware the simple design is scratched into the soft clay and cobalt blue is painted in the scratches.

Height 3⅜″.

Left to right: 20009, 20008   Left to right: 20030, 20021

PEPPER SHAKER 20019* & SALT SHAKER 20020
A Staffordshire shaker now used in the Wythe House dining room was copied for these charming adaptations. The original, made about 1760, was decorated with enamel; the adaptations have a scratch blue design.

Height 5″.
Height 5½″.

PAP BOAT 20039
This stoneware reproduction of a rare Staffordshire pap boat is molded in relief with fluting on the body and a shell motif beneath the spout. It serves as an unusual ash tray and also can be used as a pipe rest.

Length 4″.

20039

Left to right: 20019, 20020

PENNY BANK 20207
This delightful reproduction of an English eighteenth century money box is the perfect place for all your pennies. The original is dotted slipware made in Staffordshire, England.

Height 3½″.

BOWL 20205*
This piece of dotware displays an early form of slipware decoration. The dots are dark brown against a yellow background.

Height 3⅛″.

Pitcher 20202. A dotware companion to the 20205 Bowl.

Height 3⁹⁄₁₆″.

JAMESTOWN CANDLESTICK 20013
This unusual candlestick, copied after an original found in Jamestown, can add a decorative touch to any modern home. Available in yellow glaze with brown decoration.

Height 6″.

DOTWARE CANDLESTICK 20018
This charming small chamberstick was re-created from fragments excavated at the site of Anthony Hay's cabinet-making shop. It is yellow with brown dots.

Height 2½″; diameter 4½″.

20207

Left to right: 20205, 20202

Left to right: 20013, 20018

BIRD BOTTLE 20031
This novel birdhouse is a copy of an eighteenth-century bird bottle excavated in the garden of the James Geddy house. Hand-turned on a potter's wheel and fired to a rich brown glaze, it adds an authentic colonial touch to your garden. Hang it under the eaves of a building or from a tree, adding a stick for a perch.

Length 8¾″.

PIE PLATE 20025
As useful now as it was two hundred years ago, this marbleized slipware plate makes an unusual serving dish, or a fine ash tray. Its rich browns and yellows were copied from fragments unearthed in Williamsburg.

Diameter 10¼″.
Also available are two size adaptations:
20026* Medium Plate. Diameter 7½″.
20027* Small Plate. Diameter 5½″.

20031

Left to right: 20027, 20025, 20026

*Adaptation

POTPOURRI OF GIFTS

Fife and drums, and pins and things...
and books to read. As important as any
other Williamsburg reproduction and
adaptation, these small items—little
gifts to friends or yourself—spell the
meaning of Williamsburg. They add a
touch of our colonial past in a small
but significant way.

QUEEN ANNE TRIVET

This trivet is composed of the initials
"AR," representing the latin "Anna
Regina." It is the monogram of Queen
Anne, who reigned in England from
1702 until her death in 1714. Available
in brass or iron.

9" x 10½".
22010 AR Trivet, brass
23010 AR Trivet, iron

WILLIAM AND MARY TRIVET

The monogram is that of William and
Mary, who reigned jointly as sovereigns
of Great Britain from 1689 until Mary's
death in 1694. Available in brass or
iron.

6" x 8".
22011 W & M Trivet, brass
23011 W & M Trivet, iron

KING GEORGE TRIVET

Ornamented with the monogram of
George II, King of England from 1727
to 1760, this trivet is available in brass
or iron.

4" x 5".
22009 GR Trivet, brass
23009 GR Trivet, iron

COLONIAL WILLIAMSBURG
TRIVET

The initials "CW" decorate this interpretation of a cypher form that would
have been used by wealthy colonials
to mark their important possessions.
Available in brass, iron, or white
bronze.

Diameter 6".
22014 CW Trivet, brass
23014 CW Trivet, iron
22514 CW Trivet, white bronze

KING'S ARMS TRIVET

The design is taken from the coat of
arms on the sign of the famous Kings'
Arms Tavern in Williamsburg.
Available in brass or iron.

5½" x 6".
22017 KA Trivet, brass
23017 KA Trivet, iron

22010

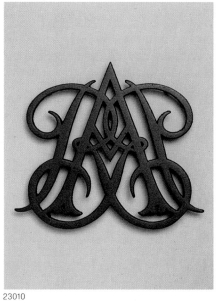

23010

23011

23009

22011

22009

23014

23017

22014

22017

CARTER'S GROVE TRIVET 22047
This elegant brass trivet was inspired by the design of the superb wood carving done on the overmantel in the parlor at Carter's Grove about 1755.

Diameter 5¾".

LION AND UNICORN PIN 22671
Copied from a keyhole escutcheon excavated at the Governor's Palace, this unusual pin is a handsome addition to a simple outfit. Polished brass.

1¾" x 2¼".

22047

22671

GEORGE WASHINGTON SILHOUETTE 22648

MARTHA WASHINGTON SILHOUETTE 22646

THOMAS JEFFERSON SILHOUETTE 22647

These cast brass silhouettes of historic Virginia personages are charming wall decorations. Easily hung, they make instant decorating accessories.

Height 5½".

Left to right: 22647, 22646, 22648

WILLIAMSBURG MACE PIN
The mace of the city of Williamsburg in miniature is available in silver or gold wash. The original bears a London silversmith's mark, dated 1749.

Length 3¾".
18048 silver
18049 gold wash

CAPITOL MACE PIN
Copied from the Capitol mace, this pin is available in gold wash or silver wash.

Length 3¼".
18120 silver
18220 gold wash

SLIPPER PIPE TAMPER 22631
A brass pipe tamper made in the shape of a lady's slipper. It is a replica of an antique.

Length 2¾".

HARLEQUIN PIPE TAMPER 22630
Copied from an early eighteenth-century "tobacco stopper," this fanciful pipe tamper is made of brass. For non-pipe smokers, the Harlequin and Slipper tampers make unusual curios for table tops or shelves.

Length 2¾".

Left to right: 18048, 18120

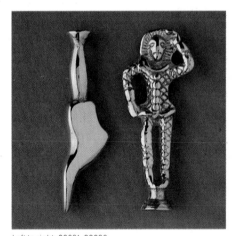

Left to right: 22631, 22630

WILLIAMSBURG LEAF TRAYS
These leaf trays are based on trees and plants which were known and grown in eighteenth-century Williamsburg. The trays make exceptionally handsome and practical ash trays.

22627 Paper Mulberry Leaf Tray. Brass; length 5½".

22666 English Primrose Leaf Tray. Brass; length 4½".

22635 American Holly Leaf Tray. Brass; length 4".

Left to right: 22627, 22666, 22635

WILLIAMSBURG HOSTESS BELL 22672
Colonial Williamsburg's hostesses, dressed in the fashion of 1760-65, inspired this delightful polished brass bell.

Height 5".

SHOEHORN 22613
This man-size brass shoehorn was copied from an antique made in England about 1750.

Length 8¼".

22672

22613

PRESSING IRON 23662
A replica of an original on exhibit in the Williamsburg Archaeological Museum, this iron is useful as a bookend or doorstop.

Length 5".

KEY 22644
A copy in brass of one of the keys to the Governor's Palace. Makes an excellent paperweight.

Length 8".

BELL METAL PORRINGER 22649
This substantial porringer is a reproduction of the antique made about 1780, now in the kitchen of Wetherburn's Tavern.

Diameter 5⅜".

HOLLY LEAF PAPER CLIP 22621
This unusual desk accessory was inspired by the American holly leaf which grows so luxuriantly in Williamsburg. It's a pretty way to keep papers in order. Polished brass.

Length 4½".

RANDOLPH PAPER CLIP 22645
The plate of this intriguing piece is an exact copy in brass of an old harness ornament bearing the Randolph crest. The base and spring have been added to make it an ideal paper clip or paperweight. 4½" x 3".

Left to right: 23662, 22644

22649

Left to right: 22621, 22645

BRASS BUCKLE 22669

An authentic copy of a colonial harness buckle, cast in brass. Its shell and C scroll motifs make it an attractive addition to your wardrobe's accessories.

5″ x 3⅛″.

BRASS BUCKLE 22670

This buckle is a copy of an eighteenth-century brass harness buckle. It can be used with an unusual effect on belts or purses.

3″ x 2⅛″.

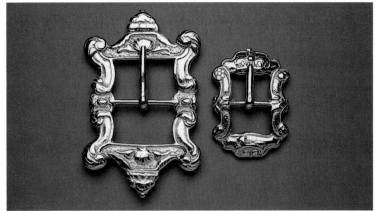

Left to right: 22669, 22670

CRYSTAL PAPERWEIGHTS

These unusual lead crystal paperweights have been created to commemorate the dying art of blown glass. Few artisans today have the required knowledge or skill to create these lovely designs. Two styles of paperweights have been made which illustrate the two different techniques in blown glass, mercury twist and air twist. Each available in three sizes.

	Small 10C	Medium 13C	Large 17C
Mercury	60550	60560	60570
Airtwist	60580	60590	60600

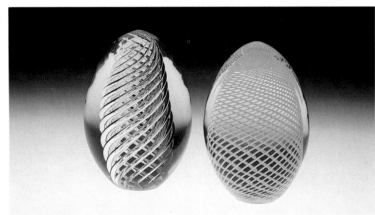

Left to right: 60590, 60560

POTPOURRI

The mixture of dried herbs, flowers, and spices in these colorful packages gives a delightful fragrance to linen closet, blanket chest, or chest of drawers. The envelopes are illustrated from a group of eighteenth-century mezzotints in the Williamsburg collection, showing the four seasons of the year.

18660 Bottle. 4½ ounces.
18667 Packet. 6½ x 5″.
18662 Sachet. 5″ x 5″.

Top: 18667   Bottom left to right: 18660, 18662

SWORD 18900

In the eighteenth century the original English sword that inspired this reproduction was referred to as an Infantry Hanger. The brass hilt and wire wrapped handle combined with the curve of the steel blade make this sword a constant reminder of our English heritage. Similar swords are displayed in the Governor's Palace.

Length 27".

18900

BROWN BESS MUSKET 18902

Know to us today as the Brown Bess musket and used throughout the eighteenth century by the British Army, they were originally called Short Land Service Muskets. The originals which were used to develop this musket (so called because the barrel is smooth bored, not rifled) are English, circa 1775. These muskets are used in the Governor's Palace in the arms arrangement that incorporates over five hundred arms in its design.

Barrel length 42"; overall length 58".

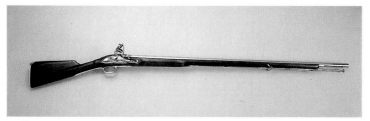

18902

PISTOL 18901

The original of this reproduction pistol was probably manufactured by Willets in the mid to late eighteenth century. These pistols retain the dignity of the original and have been used in the arms arrangements at the Governor's Palace.

Length 19".

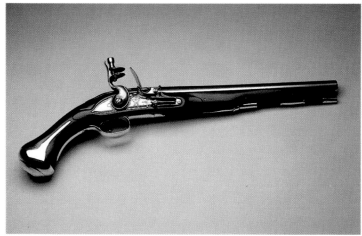

18901

BRASS JACKRACK 22609

In the late eighteenth century brass jackracks were of great importance in cooking since they were used to hang pots and kettles over a blazing fire. Today, they make handsome wall decorations that can be used for hanging plants and other decorations in the kitchen, hall, or family room. Adjustable lock position.

Backplate height 7¼"; arm projects 11".

264

CANDLE MOLDING KIT
34159
Hours of productive fun for all ages. Makes eight 10" candles just as they were made in colonial Virginia. Kit includes a reusable tin candle mold, wicking and beeswax, with complete instructions.

THE GREAT GAME OF
VISITING WILLIAMSBURG 34109
For ages 7 to 12. This exciting game takes children on a tour of historic Williamsburg, and teaches history as they play.

34159

34109

CORKSCREW 22680
Made of brass and steel, this useful tool is an authentic copy of an eighteenth-century English corkscrew

Length 5".

DECANTER LABELS 32039
These sterling silver labels with antique lettering are reproductions of those used in the eighteenth century. Available individually for Rye, Scotch, Bourbon, Port, Sherry, Brandy, Rum, Gin and Vodka, or as boxed set of six (page 232).

Label 1¾"; chain 6".

32037 Rye	32042 Brandy
32038 Scotch	32043 Gin
32039 Bourbon	32044 Rum
32040 Port	32046 Vodka
32041 Sherry	

Left to right: 22680, 32039

WILLIAMSBURG CANDLES
Medium Candles (9¼")
16004 Bayberry
16107 Beeswax

Tall Candles (12")
16412 Honey (beeswax/paraffin)
16512 White (paraffin/stearic acid)
16612 Red (paraffin/stearic acid)

Spiked Candles (8½" to fit 22233
Spiked Candlestick)
16005 Bayberry
16305 Green (bayberry/paraffin)
16408 Honey (beeswax/paraffin)
16209 White (paraffin/stearic acid)
16608 Red (paraffin/stearic acid)
16108 Beeswax

Tapers (6¾" tall to fit 22239 and
31047 Tapersticks)
16410 Honey (beeswax/paraffin)
16510 White (paraffin/stearic acid)
16610 Red (paraffin/stearic acid)
16110 Beeswax

PLACEMATS AND COASTERS

English made placemats with scenes of Williamsburg's public buildings are of heat resistant hardboard (up to 160° F) with cork backing. Placemats in set of four, coasters in sets of six. Available in parchment or green.

	Parchment	Green
Large Dinner Mats 18" x 13"	18229	18230
Small Dinner Mats 15¾" x 11¾"	18227	18228
Luncheon Mats 12" x 9"	18225	18226
Centerpiece 8⅝" x 7⅝"	18223	18224
Coasters 4⅛" x 4⅛"	18221	18222

QUEEN ANNE COASTERS 18252

These cork backed coasters are decorated with the initials "AR," representing the latin "Anna Regina." It is the monogram of Queen Anne, who reigned in England from 1702 to 1714. Set of six. Available in three colors.

4⅛" x 4⅛"

18252 Black
18253 Green
18254 Wine

CORNHUSK MAT 18024

Waste not, want not. After the corn harvest, our thrifty ancestors used the "shucks" that remained to fashion useful mats for the doorstep. Centuries later, the practicality of the cornhusk mat has not diminished.

Approximately 26" x 22".

HEARTH BROOM 18203

This version of a colonial broom is useful and charming on the hearth. It is made of undressed broom straw.

Length 26".

APPLE CONES
A beautiful centerpiece or an appealing accent on a side table or buffet, the apple cone, made of sturdy wood in two sizes, is one of Williamsburg's favorite Christmas decorations. Place bright red apples on the evenly spaced nails on the sides, add fresh greenery, and crown with the symbol of hospitality, a pineapple. Detailed instructions are included in our newest publication *Colonial Williamsburg Decorates for Christmas,* shown on page 282.

18853 Apple cone 12"
18852 Apple cone 10"

CHECKER SET 18073
The original from which this handsome wooden set is copied was probably made in England during the eighteenth century. The checkers are quite unusual because each one is decorated with an illustration from Aesop's fables.

TIN WHISTLE AND TUNE BOOK
The tin whistle or "penny flute" is a high-pitched instrument still used today in the traditional folk music of Ireland. Easily learned, it is versatile enough to challenge the serious musician. Companion music book contains 38 tunes that are also appropriate for fife, flute, and violin.

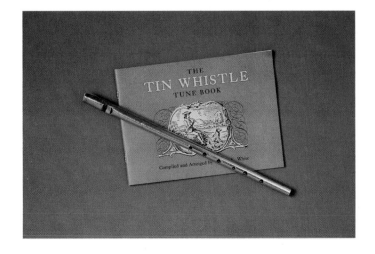

PERSIAN CARPET SCARF 18102

This screen-printed crepe silk scarf draws its design from an eighteenth-century Persian carpet in the collection of Colonial Williamsburg. The Indian influence is apparent in the eight-color design of the medallions, floral palmettes, and foliage on a blue trellis background. The wide palmette border with a floral meander subtly enhances the silk crepe scarf. 31″ x 31½″.

AVIARY HANDKERCHIEF

This cotton handkerchief is a screen-printed reproduction of an eighteenth-century English copperplate-printed handkerchief in the collection of Colonial Williamsburg. The original was known as a "snuff handkerchief." Its large size was useful during the fashionable pastime of dipping snuff, which often resulted in a sneeze.

The design on the handkerchief is educational as well as decorative. It deals with the eighteenth-century passion for aviaries, which grew out of the changing fashion in English gardening. The motif depicts a landscape illustrating various methods of catching birds. Thirteen English birds surround the scene with short instructions on their care and habits. Available in three colors 29″ x 29″.

29724 Blue
29725 Mulberry
29726 Tobacco

CW CANVAS TOTE BAG 18101

Designed to carry a multitude of extra items or double as a purse, this canvas tote has the distinctive cypher of Colonial Williamsburg printed on it.

Height 12¼″; width 9¼″; depth 5¼″.

18102

29724

18101

SCENIC TILES

Enjoy a reminder of Williamsburg with these attractive sepia tiles. Use them to protect your table from hot dishes, or as wall ornaments. Four of Colonial Williamsburg's most historic buildings are illustrated. 6″ x 6″.

18025 Capitol
18026 Governor's Palace
18027 Bruton Parish Church
18028 Raleigh Tavern

Clockwise from left: 18027, 18028, 18025, 18026

Trivet 55030

268

HERB TOWELS 29707
Six herbs and the John Blair kitchen and herb garden are printed on linen. Set of three in red, yellow and blue, one of each color. 15⅝" x 28¼".

CHARLES II PLACEMATS 29718
This striking design was taken from a wallpaper pattern of 1660. Printed in bold blue, green, charcoal or gold on fine natural linen. Mats 14" x 17"; napkins 17" square. Four mats, four napkins per set.

29716 Charcoal
29717 Gold
29718 Blue
29719 Green

**TAVERN SIGN
COCKTAIL NAPKINS**
Four of Williamsburg's famous taverns are represented: Chowning's, the Raleigh, Christiana Campbell's and the King's Arms. Sets of four or eight, in red and green, or olive and tan. 6⅝" square.

29700 Red and green, set of 8
29701 Red and green, set of 4
29702 Olive and tan, set of 8
29703 Olive and tan, set of 4

TEA TOWELS
The designs of these oversize linen tea towels are taken from tavern signs in Williamsburg.

King's Arms Tavern
Towel 29710 29½" x 19¾".

Christiana Campbell's
Tavern Towel 29708 29½" x 19¾".

Chowning's Tavern
Towel 29709 29½" x 19¾".

WILLIAMSBURG PENCIL SKETCH NOTES

Scenes of Williamsburg and the surrounding historic area decorate this selection of note papers by Charles Overly. Envelopes are included with each package of notes.

COLOR WASH NOTES 15154

A box of ten informal correspondence notes and envelopes with views of Williamsburg as sketched by Charles Overly. Each drawing has a soft color wash of either blue or yellow. 4⅝″ x 6⅛″.

SKETCH NOTES 15016

Twelve different sketches of Williamsburg's buildings, gardens, and interiors capture the spirit of the restored town. 4″ x 4¾″.

SKETCH NOTES 15029

Twelve sketches of eight Williamsburg scenes are delightful reminders of a visit to the colonial capital. 3½″ x 4½″.

RECIPE NOTES 15070

Your message to friends will be doubly welcome with this nostalgic notepaper. Williamsburg kitchens and taverns are illustrated, and each scene is accompanied by an authentic eighteenth-century recipe. A box includes ten notes. 5½″ x 8¼″.

POST PAPER

This fine quality stationery was copied by Sheaffer-Eaton from antique letter paper in the archives of Colonial Williamsburg. Its charming package is tied with red ribbon and sealed with wax.

15136 Note Paper.
30 sheets, 20 envelopes; 5″ x 8″.

15135 Letter Paper.
24 sheets and envelopes; 8″ x 12″.

JAMESTOWN, WILLIAMSBURG, YORKTOWN NOTES 15103

Twelve folded notes show views of important scenes in the "historic triangle," from the Jamestown Fort and famed Williamsburg Buildings to Yorktown's Moore House. 3¾″ x 7¼″.

TAVERN SIGN NOTES 15147

Four-fold note paper decorated with signs of the four taverns of Williamsburg and a view of Duke of Gloucester Street. All in soft pastels. Twelve notes and envelopes to the box. 6″ x 4½″.

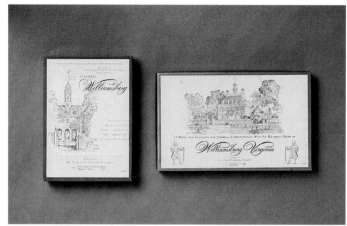

Left to right: 15154, 15016

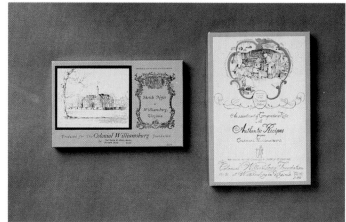

Left to right: 15029, 15070

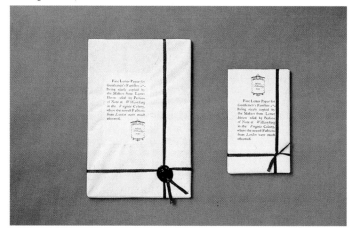

Left to right: 15135, 15136

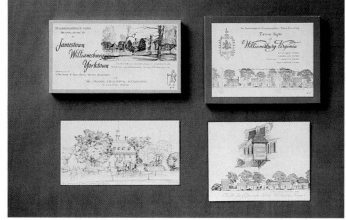

Left to right: 15103, 15147

KEDRON NOTE CARDS 15072

Charming notecards with envelopes, each one a tiny work of art. Itinerant painter Anne Bell Robb visited Williamsburg to paint the views seen here. Says she, "Williamsburg is a place set apart in time, preserved . . . where pace is slowed by cobblestone paths and garden fences . . . where past is present . . . where mood is cast in brick and weathered boards and flowered patchwork . . . where candlelight softens edges and recalls a gentler time." 5 assorted views.

CARTER'S GROVE MEMO BOX 15073
GOVERNOR'S PALACE MEMO BOX 15075
WREN BUILDING MEMO BOX 15074

Always handy for jotting down reminders to oneself or for writing brief messages to others, memo paper should be kept by a telephone or on a desk in the kitchen, office, or library. These attractive memo boxes feature drawings of three famous landmarks of the Historic Area-the Wren Building at the College of William and Mary, the Governor's Palace, and Carter's Grove plantation. 5⅛" x 6¼".

Clockwise from left: 15073, 15074, 15075.

FLOWERS OF COLONIAL WILLIAMSBURG FOLD & SEAL NOTES 15211

Popular flowers known in Williamsburg in the eighteenth-century decorate these convenient notes. Twelve notes in a package. 6" x 9".

BIRDS OF COLONIAL WILLIAMSBURG FOLD & SEAL NOTES 15222

Familiar birds frequently seen in Williamsburg provide the theme for these decorative notes. Ten notes in a package. 6" x 9".

Top to bottom: 15211, 15222.

ANIMALS AND CALLIGRAPHY
LETTER PAPER 15262

ANIMALS AND CALLIGRAPHY
NOTES 15261
The design was taken from a page
border of a book printed in England
between 1745 and 1765. There is a page
from this book, which was engraved by
George Bickham, in the Colonial
Williamsburg collection. Bickham was
well known in London for his writing
books, which were used for handwriting
practice.

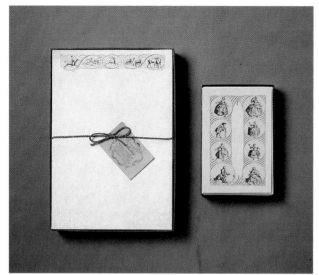

Left to right: 15262, 15261

MADISON LETTER PAPER 15227
Sixteen sheets of paper hand-bordered
in gold are boxed with sixteen charming envelopes lined with a design taken
from a reproduction wallpaper. The
original probably of French origin
dates in the early nineteenth century.
Included for longer letters are nine
plain sheets of paper.

FLORAL STRIPE NOTES 15264
The design of this note paper was de-
rived from a late eighteenth-century
French block printed fabric in the
Colonial Williamsburg collection.

PARSLEY NOTES 15263
The design of this notepaper was
developed from a fabric found in a
Dutch swatch book in the collection of
Colonial Williamsburg. The book,
dating from 1790 to 1820, was used by
merchants and customers in choosing
textile patterns.

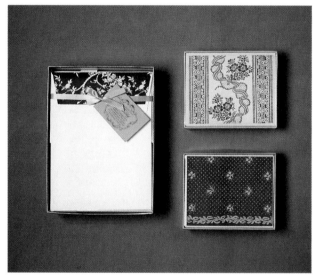

Clockwise from left: 15227, 15264, 15263

SKETCH PORTFOLIO 58330
These four pencil sketches were care-
fully reproduced from fine drawings by
Charles Overly. Views of Bruton
Parish Church, Wren Building, Capitol
and Governor's Palace are included.

11½" x 15" including margins.

58330

272

NEEDLEWORK BY
ELSA WILLIAMS
Needlework in the eighteenth century
was an art form as well as a housewife's
diversion. Faithful copies and adaptations in color and form of handsome
examples in the Colonial Williamsburg
collection are now available for today's
creative woman.

CREWEL BASKET DESIGN 29007
This charming basket of flowers was
adapted from the center of a bed
counterpane embroidered with crewels
on a twilled linen and cotton ground.
The antique is probably French and
dates from the middle of the eighteenth
century. Most of the work is in satin
stitch and French knots.

Kit contains 100% wool crewel yarn,
needle, directions and finishing
instructions.

Design size 14½" x 18".

CREWELWORK BELLPULL
KIT 29006
The floral patterns of this bellpull
were borrowed from the embroidery
found on a lady's silk apron made about
1720. Bellpulls were used in the early
nineteenth century for summoning
servants, but today they make attractive wall decorations. Kit contains a
4¾" x 41¼" design printed on 9" x 47"
natural linen twill, 100% wool crewel
yarn, needle, directions, and finishing
instructions.

FLORAL CANVASWORK 29201
Bright and bold are the colors of this
floral design reproduced from a pair of
English chair seats made about 1740-
1760. Its unusually large size will allow
upholstery of a chair, bench, or fire
screen, as well as finishing a large
pillow. The kit contains the design
21" x 18½" handpainted on 27" x 24"
#13 mono canvas, 5-ply Persian yarn to
work the design only, needle, complete
directions and stitch instructions. The
dark jade green background color
shown here matches that of the antique, but let your own good taste
dictate the choice.

29007

29201

29006

273

FLORAL CREWELWORK, I 29002
FLORAL CREWELWORK, II 29003
FLORAL CREWELWORK, III 29004
Floral motifs, reproduced from a fragmentary New England coverlet dating from 1740-1780, are worked in shades of blue and rusty rose in a variety of stitches. Perfect for pillow tops, pictures, or pieced together with fabric for a bed cover. Each kit contains two designs screened on 12″ square cream colored linen, 100% wool crewel yarn, needle, and instructions

29002

29002

29003

29003

29004

29004

THE CAPITOL 29104
GOVERNOR'S PALACE 29103
BRUTON PARISH CHURCH 29102
Well-known Williamsburg buildings are the subject of these counted cross-stitch commemorative pictures worked in four shades of sepia. Each finished design measures 13″ square. Kits include design chart, pure even-weave linen fabric, cotton floss, needle, and instructions.

29104

29103

29102

HOUSE ON HILL SAMPLER 29101
A cupola of flowers is a decidedly imaginative touch in this counted cross stitch kit, based on an original Quaker-style sampler now in the textile collection of Colonial Williamsburg. Includes chart to work finished design 22″ x 12½″, white cotton Hardanger fabric, cotton floss, needle, and complete directions.

DOMESTIC SAMPLER 29100
Typical of the kind of needlework done by young girls in Quaker schools, this attractive counted cross stitch sampler has been adapted from an antique made about 1820. Kit includes a chart to work finished design 18″ x 9¾″, white cotton Hardanger fabric, cotton floss, needle, and complete directions.

THE FARM SAMPLER 29005
The Farm. Embroidering a sampler was both an act of creativity and a test of the skill with the needle for a young lady of the eighteenth century, and in 1779 twelve-year-old Sarah Salter completed the delightful original from which this reproduction kit is taken. Its name derives from the charming pastoral scene where farm animals and birds coexist peacefully in early green summer. The kit from Elsa Williams contains a 16″ x 15¾″ design printed on 21″ x 20″ cream colored linen, cotton floss, needle, and instructions.

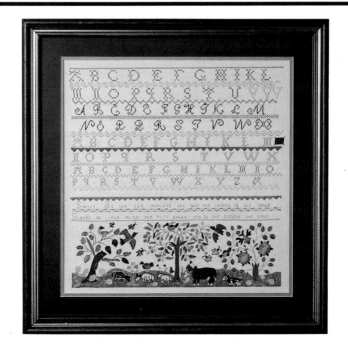

THE CHASE SAMPLER 29001

Embroidering a sampler was both an act of creativity and a test of her skill with a needle for a young lady of the eighteenth century. In 1760, eleven-year-old Mary Starker combined alphabet lists with an embroidered picture of bunnies and birds, fruits and flowers, and an utterly delightful stag and dog, caught forever in "The Chase." The variety of stitches worked in gay colors presents a challenge to the twentieth-century needle-worker who will wish to personalize the work with name and date just as Mary did. The kit includes the 16″ x 24″ design hand-printed on pure cream colored linen, cotton floss, needle, diagrams, directions, and stitch instructions.

SAMPLER KITS

These three colorful samplers are easy to work, yet look delightfully complex when completed, framed and hung on the wall. Each kit contains a stamped sampler on 100% Belgian linen, cotton floss and instructions. Frames not included.

Design size 9″ x 11½″.

29107 Boy and Girl
29105 Governor's Palace
29106 Bruton Parish Church

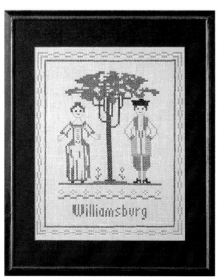

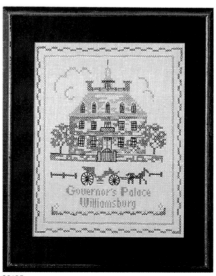

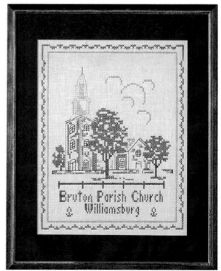

29107

29105

29106

276

CANVASWORK CHAIR SEAT 29204

This canvaswork kit is taken from an English needlework chair seat in the collection at Colonial Williamsburg. The antique dates from the 1740's and is worked in wool covering the linen canvas. A variety of stitches was used, including cross, tent, and gobelin. A fascinating detail on the antique is that the ground is worked in one color in Irish stitch, which runs both vertically and horizontally.

#13 White mono canvas size 27″ x 27″. Design size 16″ x 18″.

FLORAL CUSHION TOP 29200

Pumpkin and plum, strawberry and salmon—a wide palette of colors all come together for a dazzling effect in this oversized cushion top copied from an English canvas work in the Colonial Williamsburg textile collection. The kit contains a design 21″ x 13¼″ hand-painted on 30″ x 27″ #17 pure linen canvas, large enough to upholster a chair or bench as well as finish a large pillow. Included are 5-ply Persian and crewel yarns to work the design, needle, complete directions and stitch instructions. Background yarn is not included. The gold background color shown here matches that of the antique.

FLORENTINE CUSHION TOP KIT 29202
FLORENTINE BENCH TOP KIT 29203

The beauty of Irish stitch, today called Florentine or "flame-stitch" work was familiar in colonial times. Adapted from an eighteenth-century silk-on-linen cushion, this kit contains a chart to work finished design 14¾″ x 18½″, pure linen canvas, 17 threads per inch, 100% wool 5-ply Persian yarn, needle, and instructions. This pattern is also available as a kit to make a 20″ x 24″ design, suitable for footstool or bench cover.

29202

WALLPAPER MINIATURES:
Developed from full size Colonial Williamsburg reproduction and adaptation wallpapers, these miniature papers have been scaled for use in a miniature room or doll house. They are the perfect decorating accessory in the creation of an authentic miniature eighteenth century room. Packed two 12″ x 18″ sheets each pattern.

92800 Lafayette Floral
92801 Winterberry
92802 Brighton
92803 Stencil Square
92804 Madison
92805 Calico Bird
92806 Fox Grape
92820 Williamsburg Apples
92821 Bluebell Stripe
92840 Little Crowns—Gold
92841 Little Crowns—Red

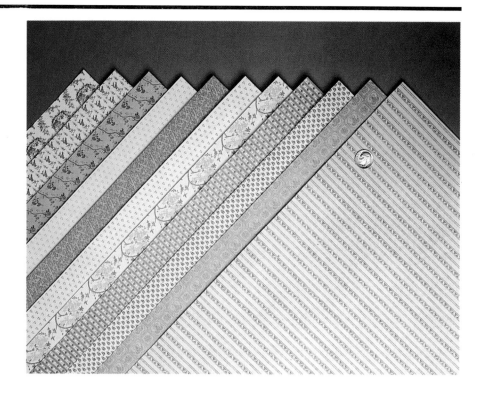

PEWTER MINIATURES
Pewter miniatures of 1/12 scale are the perfect accessory in creating a miniature period room. English and American antiques have been faithfully copied to produce these miniatures, which retain the integrity of the original pieces.

STERLING SILVER QUEEN ANNE MINIATURE PLACE SETTING
This miniature sterling silver place setting reflects the popular design of the original eighteenth-century flatware. The full scale reproduction of this place setting may be seen on page 231. 1/12 scale.

92030 Candlesticks
92054 Strawberry Dish
92095 Pitcher
92098 Open Salt and Pepper Caster
92055 Tankard
92096 Salt and Pepper Caster
92059 Plate
92400 Silver Queen Ann Place Setting
3 Pieces
92078 Inkwell with Quill
92060 Porringer
92087 Chamberstick
92079 Tray

Dime included for size perspective.

Clockwise from left: 92095, 92030, 92098, 92054.

Clockwise from left: 92096, 92055, 92400, 92059, 92400.

Clockwise from left: 92078, 92079, 92087, 92060.

RECORD ALBUMS†

A WILLIAMSBURG CANDLELIGHT CONCERT 4000
The Palace Orchestra, directed by Cary McMurran, presents a program of outstanding works known to have been performed in eighteenth-century Williamsburg. A collector's item for those who appreciate the music of the period and/or have enjoyed a memorable evening at a Candlelight Concert at the Governor's Palace. Stereo (compatible with monaural needle).

FIFES & DRUMS 40003
Colonial Williamsburg's unique Band of Musick offers popular eighteenth-century tunes performed on instruments of the period, and the Fife & Drum Corps plays the stirring martial music of 200 years ago. Stereo (compatible with monaural needle).

O COME SWEET MUSIC 40006
This recording gives an enticing "taste" of the wide variety of music known during the many decades when Britain ruled these colonies. More important, it revives the spirit and enthusiasm for part singing that existed two centuries ago. Stereo (compatible with monaural needle).

AN EVENING OF MUSIC AT CARTER'S GROVE PLANTATION 40002
Ann Rowe, Mezzo-soprano,
J. S. Darling, Harpsichord,
Elizabeth Chapman, Violin, and
Frances Hooper, Violoncello.

This record, made at Carter's Grove, a plantation just below Williamsburg on the James River, presents an evening of music as it might have occurred two hundred years ago.

Miss Rowe acts as Colonial Williamsburg's singer in residence, Mrs. Chapman and Mrs. Hooper regularly play in the Governor's Palace ensemble, and Mr. Darling is the organist of Bruton Parish Church.

THE MUSIC TEACHER 40005
Colonial Virginians enjoyed music and many were accomplished performers. Versatile music teachers provided instruction especially to middle and upper class families. In addition to the harpsichord, guitars, recorders, violins, violas da gamba, and other instruments were well known—as were composers Schickhardt, Pepusch, Teleman, and Loeillet. This recording made at Williamsburg features the staff of the music teacher's shop—a regular presentation for visitors.

THE WREN CHAPEL ORGAN 40009
The Wren Building of the College of William and Mary in Williamsburg—the oldest surviving collegiate structure in the United States—contains a chapel restored in the style of English universities. In its west gallery stands an organ (circa 1760), which is still used today for religious services and recitals of period music. J. S. Darling is the performer on this record. The selections include a number of voluntaries, known to the Virginia colonists, and such favorites as the Prince of Denmark's March and Old Hundredth.

SONGS OF LIBERTY 40008
This collection of song and instrumental music relating to the American Revolution is performed by the choirs of Bruton Parish Church in Williamsburg. As the colonies reacted to events of the times, it was natural that musicians expressed in song the attitudes of the patriots. Many pieces were composed for the man "first in the hearts of his countrymen" like Washington's March, here performed on an antique pipe organ, and The Battle of Trenton, played on a 1762 Kirchman harpsichord. Three versions of The Star Spangled Banner conclude the record, Adams and Liberty, The Anacreontic Song, and the 1814 words by Francis Scott Key which became our national anthem.

MR. JEFFERSON'S MUSIC 40004
Thomas Jefferson regarded music as "a delightful recreation through life" and "this favorite passion of my soul."

Jefferson catalogued his large collection of music in 1783. The selections heard on this record are representative of his preferences. With the exception of the Handel anthem, which required both orchestra and choir, it is likely that Jefferson and his family played all of the pieces on this recording.

A CONCERT OF MILITARY MUSIC 40010
In the eighteenth century, fifers and drummers regulated the routine of camp life, waking the troops with the morning reveille and beating a tattoo at day's end.

Many of the pieces are adaptations of dance tunes and were played at evening entertainments to bolster the troops' esprit de corps or at dances given by the officers.

The performers are the Senior Fife and Drum Corps of the Colonial Williamsburg Foundation who perform regularly for Williamsburg visitors.

COLONIAL SINGING GAMES AND DANCES 40001
This instructional record is intended for use in elementary schools. It is accompanied by a comprehensive pamphlet containing directions for performing the games and dances as well as facsimiles of the music in many instances. The subject has been carefully researched and field tested. The games, dances, and music are those believed to be preferred by the American colonists in the eighteenth century.

PETER PELHAM'S MUSIC 40011
A recital of pieces known to the chief musician of eighteenth-century Williamsburg is played in Bruton Parish Church. The selections include serious and popular works of the Virginia colony at the time of the American Revolution. Mr. Pelham, Bruton's first organist, performed for services and recitals for more than forty-five years. His only surviving composition, a minuet, is included on the recording.

BOOKS ON
THE DECORATIVE ARTS
BY COLONIAL WILLIAMSBURG
EXPERTS

CHELSEA PORCELAIN
AT WILLIAMSBURG 11006
By John C. Austin
Colonial Williamsburg has amassed an outstanding collection of ceramics produced by the Chelsea Porcelain Manufactory during its years of operation, 1745-1769, which is described and illustrated in this catalog. A facsimile reproduction of the 1755 Chelsea sale catalog is included as the appendix.
78 color plates; 73 black and white illustrations.
240 pages, 8 x 11¼.

REBELLION AND
RECONCILIATION: SATIRICAL
PRINTS ON THE REVOLUTION
AT WILLIAMSBURG 11036
By Joan D. Dolmetsch
A selection of 100 political "cartoons" from the Colonial Williamsburg print collection: English and Continental comment in pictorial form pertaining to the American Revolution. Descriptive text on historical setting and significance accompanies each print.
101 black and white illustrations.
230 pages, 9½ x 8½.

DECORATED FIREARMS, 1540-1870,
FROM THE COLLECTION OF
CLAY P. BEDFORD 11010
By Wallace B. Gusler and
James D. Lavin
Outstanding examples of decorated firearms from the collection of Clay P. Bedford are examined in ninety-four detailed entries. Mainly European in origin, the arms were carefully chosen to illustrate the decorative evolution of Western firearms over more than three centuries. 102 color plates; 166 black and white illustrations.
254 pages, 11 x 9½.

EIGHTEENTH-CENTURY PRINTS
IN COLONIAL AMERICA:
TO EDUCATE AND
DECORATE 11058
Edited by Joan D. Dolmetsch, with an introduction by Graham Hood
Prints are an excellent source of visual information about the eighteenth century. These heavily illustrated essays were originally given at the 1974 Print Conference held at Colonial Williamsburg. 108 black and white illustrations.
224 pages, 9¼ x 6⅛.

ENGLISH AND ORIENTAL
CARPETS AT WILLIAMSBURG
By Mildred B. Lanier
A catalog illustrating and analyzing the imported floor coverings assembled over the past forty years by the Colonial Williamsburg Department of Collections. 57 color plates; 6 black and white illustrations.
146 pages, 8 x 11¼.

FURNITURE OF WILLIAMSBURG
AND EASTERN VIRGINIA
1710-1790 11059
By Wallace B. Gusler
In response to the need to underscore the importance of the decorative arts in American culture, an exhibition of the fine products of Virginia's colonial cabinetmakers was organized by Wallace B. Gusler, curator of furniture at Colonial Williamsburg. He has assembled the results of his research in this comprehensive volume, which deals not only with the objects displayed in the exhibition, but also with other examples of colonial furniture. New insights are offered into the astonishing craftsmanship of Virginia's leading colonial cabinetmakers: Peter Scott, Anthony Hay, Benjamin Bucktrout and Edmund Dickinson.
194 pages, 9 x 11.

NEW ENGLAND FURNITURE AT
WILLIAMSBURG 11031
By Barry A. Greenlaw
A descriptive and illustrated catalog of 164 articles of furniture made in New England and now in the Colonial Williamsburg collection. 8 color plates; 183 black and white illustrations.
208 pages, 8 x 11¼.

ENGLISH SILVER AT
WILLIAMSBURG 11217
By John D. Davis
With more than 1100 black and white illustrations, this catalog describes 274 articles on English-made silver and plated silverware in the Colonial Williamsburg collection, most dating from the eighteenth century.
262 pages, 8 x 11¼.

A CHECKLIST OF AMERICAN
COVERLET WEAVERS 11057
By John W. Heisey, Gail C. Andrews, and Donald R. Walters
The book consists of an alphabetical checklist that cites biographical and technical information on over 900 weavers. A short glossary of terms and a list of public coverlet collections is also included. 10 color plates; 118 black and white illustrations, 2 drawings, map.
162 pages, 8¼ x 10½.

CHARLES BRIDGES AND
WILLIAM DERING: TWO
VIRGINIA PAINTERS,
1735-1750 11005
By Graham Hood
An examination of all that is known of the lives and careers of two of the earliest artists in Virginia to whom documented portraits are attributed. All the known portraits attributed to these two painters are illustrated.
9 color plates; 76 black and white illustrations.
142 pages, 7½ x 10¼.

Top, left to right: 11006, 11036, 11010, 11058, 11014   Bottom, left to right: 11059, 11031, 11217, 11057, 11005

COLONIAL WILLIAMSBURG
ARCHAEOLOGICAL SERIES
A series of softbound books presenting
the results of archaeological excavations and research carried out in
Williamsburg and its environs from
the earliest days of the restoration.

GLASS IN COLONIAL
WILLIAMSBURG'S
ARCHAEOLOGICAL
COLLECTIONS 11222
By Ivor Noël Hume. 40 illustrations,
48 pages.

POTTERY AND PORCELAIN IN
COLONIAL WILLIAMSBURG'S
ARCHAEOLOGICAL
COLLECTIONS 11237
By Ivor Noël Hume. 43 illustrations,
48 pages.

ARCHAEOLOGY AND
WETHERBURN'S TAVERN 11205
By Ivor Noël Hume. 37 illustrations,
48 pages.

THE WELLS OF WILLIAMSBURG:
COLONIAL TIME CAPSULES 11248
By Ivor Noël Hume. 47 illustrations,
48 pages.

JAMES GEDDY AND SONS:
COLONIAL CRAFTSMEN 11226
By Ivor Noël Hume. 45 illustrations,
48 pages.

WILLIAMSBURG
CABINETMAKERS:
THE ARCHAEOLOGICAL
EVIDENCE 11250
By Ivor Noël Hume. 46 illustrations,
48 pages.

ARCHAEOLOGY AND THE
COLONIAL GARDENER 11204
By Audrey Noël Hume. 58 illus-
trations, 96 pages.

DIGGING FOR
CARTER'S GROVE 11216
By Ivor Noël Hume. 42 illustrations,
color foldout map of plantation,
64 pages.

FOOD 11257
By Audrey Noël Hume. 45 illustrations, 68 pages.

COLONIAL WILLIAMSBURG
OCCASIONAL PAPERS IN
ARCHAEOLOGY

EARLY ENGLISH DELFTWARE
FROM LONDON AND
VIRGINIA 11012
By Ivor Noël Hume
The author has assembled the results
of nearly twenty years' research that
began in London with excavations in
the vicinity of the Pickleherring delftware manufactory, established about
1612. Its owner, Christian Wilhelm,
became a business associate of a
seventeenth-century Virginia governor,
Sir John Harvey, and thus forged an
historical and archaeological link
between delftwares from the London
kilns and those used and discarded in
Virginia. 7 color plates; 77 black and
white illustrations.
136 pages, 8½ x 11.

FIVE ARTIFACT STUDIES 11016
By Audrey Noël Hume, Merry W.
Abbitt, Robert H. McNulty,
Isabel Davies, and Edward Chappell.
The authors describe and analyze the
contents of a well, eighteenth-century
shoe buckles, bayonets, window glass,
and horseshoes.
61 illustrations, 124 pages, 8½ x 11.

Top, left to right: 11222, 11237, 11205, 11248, 11226, 11250   Bottom, left to right: 11012, 11204, 11216, 11257, 11016

POPULAR TITLES PUBLISHED BY
COLONIAL WILLIAMSBURG
For a complete listing of Colonial
Williamsburg publications write
Craft House, Post Office Box CH,
Williamsburg, Virginia 23187

CHRISTMAS DECORATIONS
FROM WILLIAMSBURG'S FOLK
ART COLLECTION 11007
This how-to craft book contains easy
to follow instructions for making 90
decorations, many based on traditional
folk crafts. Utilizing natural materials
—nuts, cones, pine needles, cornhusks,
and shells—and other basic supplies
readily available in most homes, the
ornaments range from simple ones that
children can make to more complex
decorations that will appeal to adults.
Step-by-step drawings and a black and
white photograph of the finished
decoration accompany each set of
instructions. Twenty-eight of the ornaments are also illustrated in full color.

80 pages, 8¼ x 11.

A WILLIAMSBURG
CHRISTMAS 11061
Text by Donna C. Sheppard
Photography by Frank J. Davis and
Robert Llewellyn
Sketches by Vernon Wooten
Christmas is the most festive season in
Williamsburg, the restored eighteenth-
century capital of colonial Virginia.
A Williamsburg Christmas captures the
excitement of the holidays from the
moment the Grand Illumination of
the old city ushers in the season with
singing, dancing, and music. Featured
are the beautiful wreaths and other
decorations long associated with
Colonial Williamsburg, "groaning
boards" laden with delicacies for holiday feasting, and the many activities
that make Christmas in Williamsburg
unique. Illustrations of interior and
exterior decorations sure to inspire
ideas for anyone's front door or table,
charming line drawings scattered
throughout, and recipes for such elegant holiday treats as champagne
sherbet and eggnog made the southern
way add to the appeal of this book.
A Williamsburg Christmas is truly an
adventure into the world of Christmas
past, a world that may still be enjoyed
in this special town today. 124 full-
color photographs; 8 sketches.

84 pages, 9¼ x 9¼.

COLONIAL WILLIAMSBURG
OFFICIAL GUIDEBOOK
AND MAP 11215
Here is Colonial Williamsburg, street
by street, house by house, with the
intimate story of each building and
shop in terms of the people who lived
and worked in eighteenth-century
Williamsburg. 146 illustrations.
Color map.

110 pages, 5¼ x 7⅝.

THE WILLIAMSBURG
COLLECTION OF ANTIQUE
FURNISHINGS 11050
A graphic overview of the many
varieties of objects assembled during
the past four decades to furnish
Colonial Williamsburg's 200 exhibition rooms. With an introduction
analyzing the curatorial program—past,
present, and planned. 216 full-color
illustrations.

120 pages, 8¼ x 11.

Top, left to right: 11007, 11061, 11215   Bottom, left to right: 11050, 11223, 11218

PLANTS OF COLONIAL
WILLIAMSBURG: HOW TO
IDENTIFY 200 OF COLONIAL
AMERICA'S FLOWERS, HERBS,
AND TREES 11223
By Joan Parry Dutton
Illustrations by Marion Ruff Sheehan
This updated guide to the plants in
Colonial Williamsburg's gardens des-
cribes and discusses 200 plants, 191 of
which are illustrated in full color.
Mrs. Dutton gives the historical back-
ground of each plant to link it to the
colonial period. Brief biographies of
early plantsmen explain the roles they
played in the history of horticulture.
191 full-color illustrations.

200 pages, 4½ x 8.

THE FLOWER WORLD OF
WILLIAMSBURG 11218
By Joan Parry Dutton
Describes the eighteenth-century
English garden scene and its impact on
the Virginia colony; the exchange of
plants between the Old World and
the New; the part played by plant
collectors and explorers; the far-famed
flower arrangements seen in Colonial
Williamsburg; and original flower con-
tainers used. One chapter is devoted
to dried plant material. Revised
edition. 40 full-color illustrations.

144 pages, 7 x 10.

THE GARDENS OF
WILLIAMSBURG 11219
An examination, with 90 full-color
photographs, of Williamsburg's formal
gardens and open greens and their
place in the life of the eighteenth-
century capital.

48 pages, 8 x 10½.

LEGACY FROM THE PAST 11229
A portfolio of the 88 original eighteenth-century and early nineteenth-
century buildings in or near the
Historic Area of Williamsburg illustrated in 138 full-color photographs.

78 pages, 8¼ x 11.

THE WILLIAMSBURG ART
OF COOKERY 11048
By Helen Bullock
This volume enables the modern
housewife to offer the same time-
tested fare that pleased our colonial
ancestors. Includes a table of favorite
garden herbs. Eighteenth-century
typography, thirteenth printing. 5 line
drawings.

276 pages, 4 x 6⅞.

THE WILLIAMSBURG
COOKBOOK 11051
A collection of 195 traditional and
contemporary recipes initially compiled
and adapted by Letha Booth and the
staff of Colonial Williamsburg, with
commentary by Joan Parry Dutton.
Updated and enlarged. 11 full-color
illustrations by Taylor Biggs Lewis, Jr.;
40 line drawings by Vernon E. Wooten.

172 pages, 7 x 10.

A WINDOW ON
WILLIAMSBURG 11253
By Taylor Biggs Lewis, Jr.,
John J. Walklet, Jr., and
Thomas K. Ford
An intimate glimpse of restored
Williamsburg, its gardens and greens,
its buildings great and small, its crafts,
and its people. Revised edition.
122 photographs in full color.

80 pages, 7½ x 9¾.

COLONIAL WILLIAMSBURG
DECORATES FOR
CHRISTMAS 11262
By Libbey Hodges Oliver
Colonial Williamsburg is famous for
the wreaths and other exterior and
interior decorations that adorn its
houses, shops, and exhibition buildings
at Christmas. This how-to book contains directions for making 60 beautiful
decorations. Included are old favorites
like the apple cone, and new adaptations like an herb wreath. Kissing balls,
accents for banisters and sconces,
mantel and table arrangements, a special section on dried materials, and, of
course, a wide selection of Williamsburg's famous wreaths are featured.
Step by step drawings and fifty full-
color illustrations show how to create
each decoration at home.

80 pages, 8 x 10½.

Top, left to right: 11219, 11229, 11048   Bottom, left to right: 11051, 11253, 11262

INDEX

DIRECTIONS FOR ORDERING

An order blank and a postage-saver envelope are enclosed for your convenience. Please furnish your name and address (including Zip Code Number), as well as catalogue number and description of articles ordered.

All prices quoted include shipping charges by usual methods. Special delivery or air mail charges will be extra.

Craft House sells at retail only.

Special prices for sets or pairs (as quoted) are for shipment to one address.

Safe delivery of shipments is guaranteed. In case of damage, please notify Craft House without delay.

Craft House will gladly forward gifts directly to your friends. Enclose your card with the order, furnishing name and address (including Zip Code Number) of the recipient.

For decorator assistance, call 1-804-229-1000 between 9:00 A.M. and 5:00 P.M. Monday through Saturday.

PRICES SUBJECT
TO CHANGE WITHOUT
NOTICE

All income derived from Craft House is used to maintain and develop Colonial Williamsburg and to carry forward its educational program.

To order by telephone: call TOLL-FREE 1-800-446-9240 for order being charged to Visa, Master Card, or American Express (Sorry-no COD). The Craft House and Colonial Williamsburg charge accounts have been discontinued. You can call 24 hours a day, seven days a week. We will handle your order personally between 9 and 5, Monday through Saturday. At night and on Sunday your order will be recorded and processed the next day.
To ensure accuracy, we suggest you fill out the order form in this catalogue then read it when you call. (Sorry-toll-free calling is not available from Alaska, Hawaii, or Virginia. To order from these states, call 1-804-229-1000, ext. 5493 Monday through Saturday 9 to 5).

CREDITS:
COLONIAL WILLIAMSBURG
Robert W. Spurgeon
Richard J. Stinely
Jackie C. Smith

SPECIAL PHOTOGRAPHY
Hedrich-Blessing
Tets Itahara
Terry Lee
Charles Shotwell

DESIGN
Mobium Corporation

PRINTING
R. R. Donnelley & Sons Company